Bert Brunet is not only a skilled field worker but an accomplished breeder, photographer and illustrator of spiders, and gives many lectures and demonstrations to schools and entomological societies. He has served as a member and honorary treasurer of the Royal Zoological Society of NSW (Entomological Section), and as honorary secretary of the Society for Insect Studies.

His books on arthropods include *One Step Closer Please, A Nature Study* and *The Silken Web*. Bert Brunet was awarded the Zoo le Souef Award in 1987. In 1995, *The Silken Web* won the Royal Zoological Society of NSW's Gilbert Whitley Award in the category of Natural History.

St Andrews Cross spider,
Argiope keyserlingi, with prey.

SPIDERWATCH

A GUIDE TO AUSTRALIAN SPIDERS

Bert Brunet

Reed New Holland

To Venus,
thank you for all your love and encouragement.

This edition published in Australia in 2000 by
Reed New Holland
an imprint of New Holland Publishers (Australia) Pty Ltd
Sydney • Auckland • London • Cape Town

14 Aquatic Drive Frenchs Forest NSW 2086 Australia
218 Lake Road Northcote Auckland New Zealand
86 Edgware Rd London W2 2EA United Kingdom
80 McKenzie Street Cape Town 8001 South Africa

First published in 1996 by Reed Books Australia

National Library of Australia
Cataloguing-in-Publication Data:

Brunet, Bert.
Spiderwatch: a guide to australian spiders.

Includes index.
ISBN(13) 978-1-87633-449-9
ISBN(10) 1 87633 449 5

1. Spiders–Australia–Identification. I. Title.

595.440994

Designer: R.T.J. Kinkhamer
Cover Designer: Peta Nugent
Illustrations: Bert Brunet
Printer: Hong Kong Graphics & Printing Ltd

15 14 13 12 11 10 9

Author photograph inside book by Lynn Brunet

CONTENTS

Acknowledgements

Many people have contributed their time, energy and supportive interest to the writing of this book. I especially thank my father Herbert William Brunet whose companionship has greatly enhanced many a field trip while studying, observing and photographing spiders. I am appreciative of the supportive interest and invaluable assistance contributed by Lynn Brunet on numerous field trips. Appreciation is also extended to my children, Alice and Daniel, who have always shown enthusiasm for learning about nature. I should also like to thank Anthony Saunders for his companionship on a number of field trips over the years; Clarry Chadwick and Michael Gray of the Australian Museum for their helpful discussions and Mark Elgar, Rachel Allen and Theo Dopheide for their constructive criticism concerning the subject. Further, I should like to thank Eugene Hodgens for his enthusiasm for the subject and for his company on many field trips. My thanks also to my editor, Gillian Gillett.

INTRODUCTION

I have prepared this handbook with the aim of presenting as complete a picture as possible (in the present state of our knowledge) of the most frequently encountered Australian spiders. Condensation and selection of suitable material has determined its content. It has not always been easy to organise the information. The apparent scarcity of readily available material on the biology of spiders reflects modern society's disregard for the spider's important ecological role in nature. Entomologists have estimated that the weight of insects consumed annually by spiders is perhaps greater than the total weight of the entire human population.

The spider's vital ecological role as a leading natural controller of agricultural, horticultural and everyday household insect pests has only recently become recognised. Without spiders, insect populations would soar, causing even more widespread famine and disease than already exists. Spiders do not eat our crops, nor do they carry or spread disease, and the poison of most spiders acts only upon small prey—only a few species possess chemicals dangerous to humans. In this present work I have chosen to represent those species which most frequently come to our attention, including those known to be dangerous. It is especially hoped that this book stimulates the reader into observing spiders. The spider fauna of Australia consists of unique arthropods worthy of respect and wonder and need not evoke superstition nor fear.

Within the code of the International Commission on Zoological Nomenclature the naming and placing of spider and insect species are being continually reviewed and revised. The enormous variety of living organisms (particularly the spiders and insects) involves many forms that do not fit neatly into the classification hierarchy. This is not surprising since millions of units are involved. However, the great diversity of spider and insect species are gradually being placed and their boundaries established.

There are 70 families of spiders presently recognised in Australia. New families and genera have been erected to accommodate new findings. The names of all families of fauna end in the letters 'idae' and each family represents a group of animals with similar characteristics (external or internal), anatomy, habits, evolutionary divergence, etc. Within these spider families of Australia are 430 recognised genera which consist of almost 2,000 described species.

After Mygalomorphs, Wolf spiders are the most common ground-dwelling spiders. They are easily distinguished from Mygalomorphs by their large eyes.

HOW TO USE THIS BOOK

Male St Andrew's Cross

Keeping up with changes in nomenclature is always important. However, in the interval between the completion of the book and its appearance in bookshops, such changes can and quite often do occur, as in the case of recent proposals for the genera of Acacia and Eucalyptus. Even then, new names may be on probation until, or if, they become revised again.

The keyguide presents a typical example of each family described in the book, with page number reference.

To help you find a particular species, I have included in the index its old Latin name along with its new name wherever applicable. For a more comprehensive account of the natural history of Australian spiders, refer to my book *The Silken Web*.

The keyguide does not imply that classification is based on behaviour, but indicates assemblages of spiders that have 'adopted' distinctive approaches to capturing prey. The known dangerous Australian spiders are also illustrated in this sequence. The natural history of spiders is not so readily disclosed by adhering strictly to lists of families alone. Headings and sub-headings styled for the snare-making spiders include the name given to the type of snare along with the common name of the spider.

Jumping spider, *Opisthoncus* species, with prey.

KEYGUIDE
Mygalomorphs (Primitive)

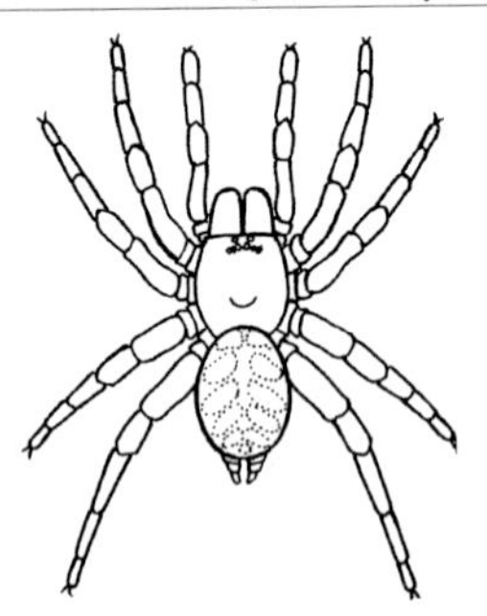

Female Trapdoor *Arbanitis*, family Idiopidae. Body length 30 mm or more. (p.81)

Male Mouse *Missulena*, family Actinopodidae. Male often bright red, yellow and blue, female dark brown. Body length 20 mm or more. (p.79)

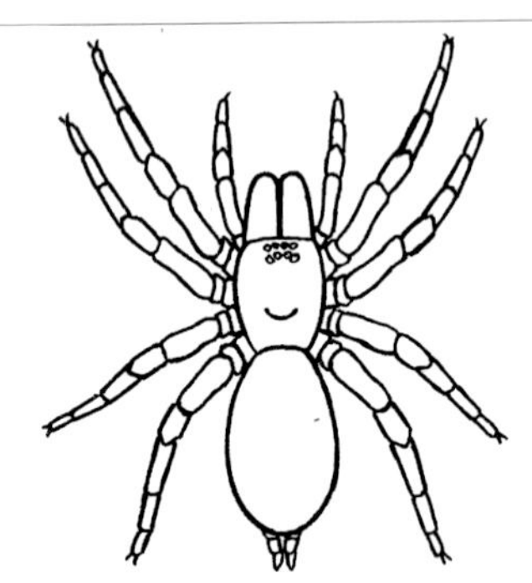

Female Funnel-web *Atrax*, family Hexathelidae. Glossy black. Body length 30 mm or more. (p.91)

Male Funnel-web *Atrax*, family Hexathelidae. Glossy black. Body length 20 mm or more. (p.91)

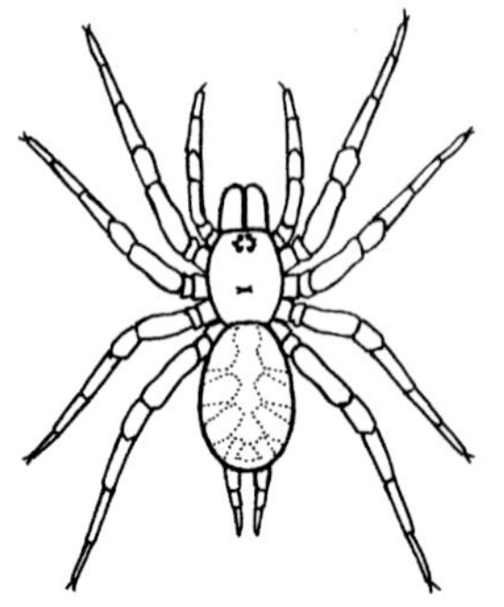

Female Funnel-web *Bymainiella*, family Hexathelidae. Brown to black. Body length 20 mm or more. (p.87)

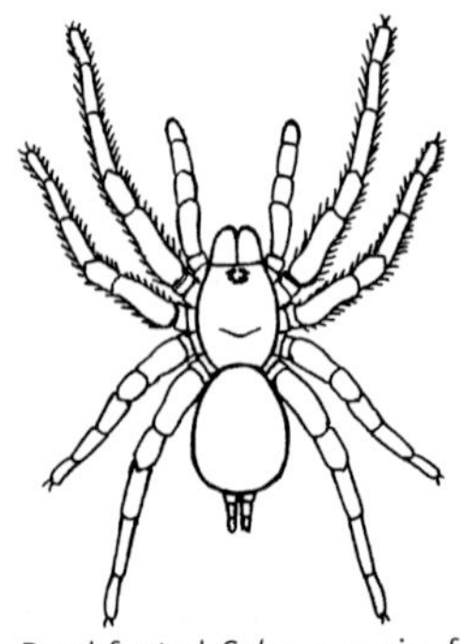

Female Brushfooted *Selenocosmia*, family Theraphosidae. Umber-red brown. Body length 40 mm or more. (p.93)

Open-range Araneomorphs (Modern)

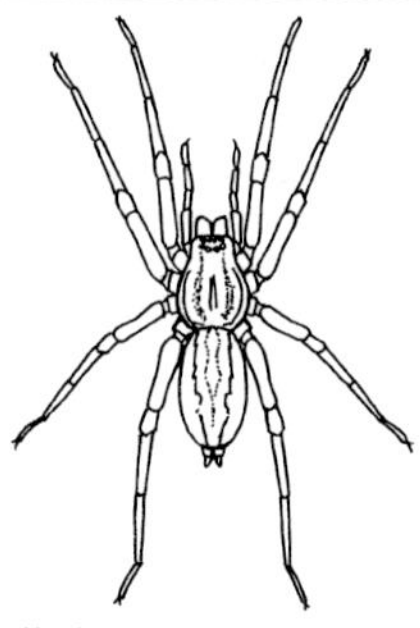

Female cylindrical Sac *Lampona* and *Cheiracanthium*, families Clubionidae and Gnaphosidae. Buff, grey or dark brown. Body length 20 mm. (p.98)

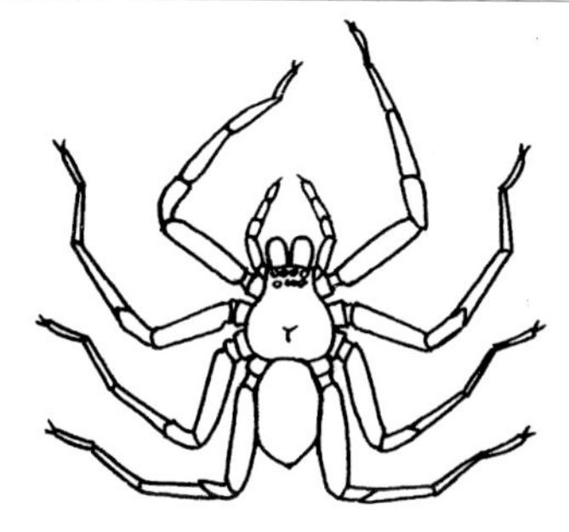

Female flat Sac *Hemicolea* and *Rebilus*, family Gnaphosidae. Ochre-brown, dark-brown or black. Body length 20 mm or more. (p.102)

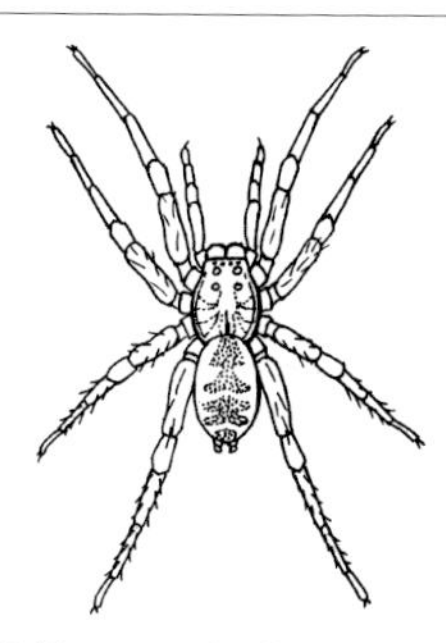

Female Wolf *Lycosa*, family Lycosidae. Patterned in many shades of brown and grey. Body length 10 mm or more. (p.106)

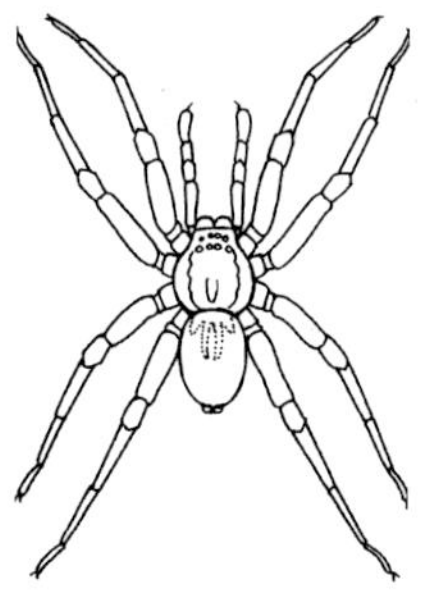

Female Nursery-web *Dolomedes*, family Pisauridae. Colouring like that of Wolf spiders, but eye formation differs. Body length up to 40 mm. (p.111)

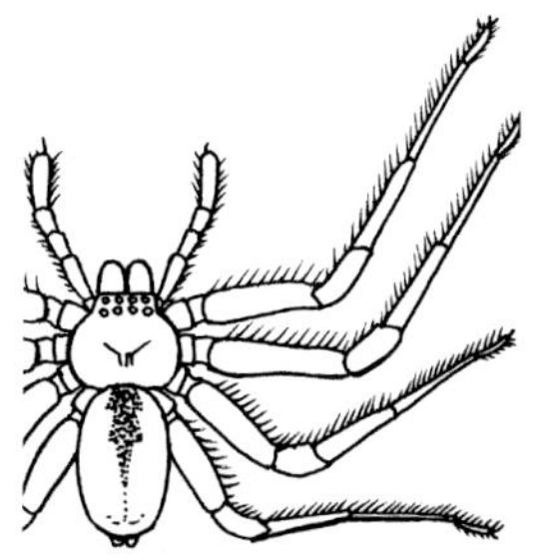

Female Huntsman *Delena* and *Selenops*, families Heteropodidae and Selenopidae. Red-brown, yellow-ochre, grey, dark and light markings, flat body and splayed legs. Body length 20 mm or more. (p.113)

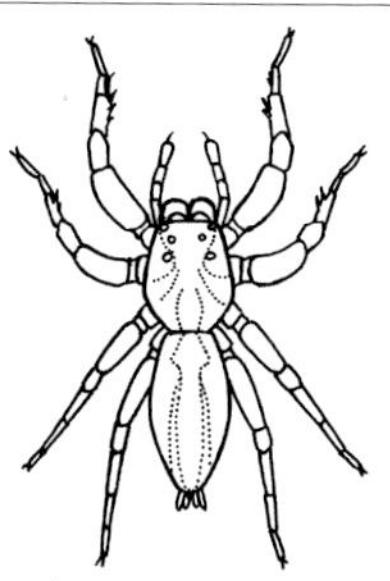

Female Jumping *Mopsus*, family Salticidae. Colouring varies greatly. Body length 8-12 mm. Large median eyes, box-shaped carapace, squat body. (p.120)

Ambushers and Anglers (Araneomorphs)

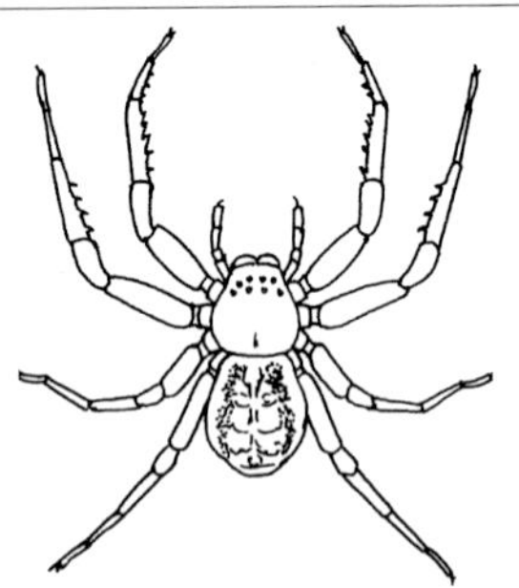

Female Crab *Diaea*, family Thomisidae. Yellow and green. Body length 10 mm or more. (p.128)

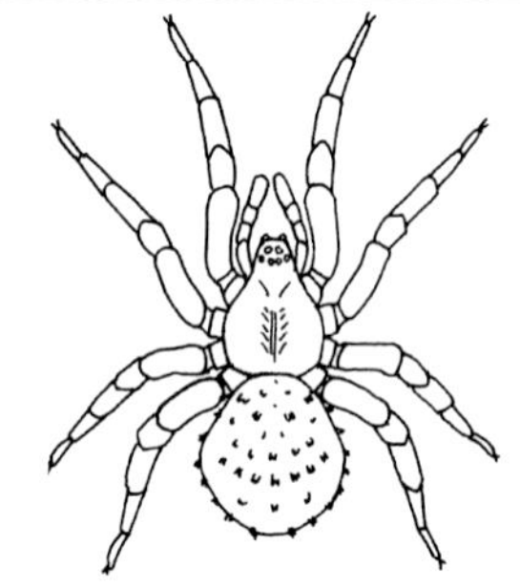

Female Cryptic Crab *Cryptothele*, family Cryptothelidae. Knobbly, green-brown or black (to match surroundings). Body length 15 mm. (p.130)

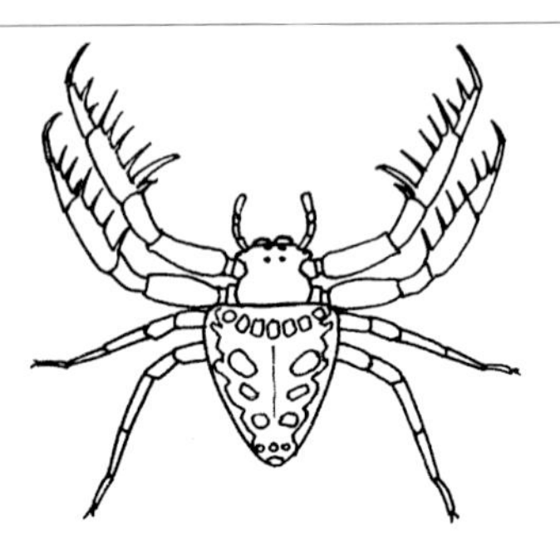

Female Triangular *Arcys*, family Araneidae. Bright red, yellow, white and black. Body length 10 mm. (p.131)

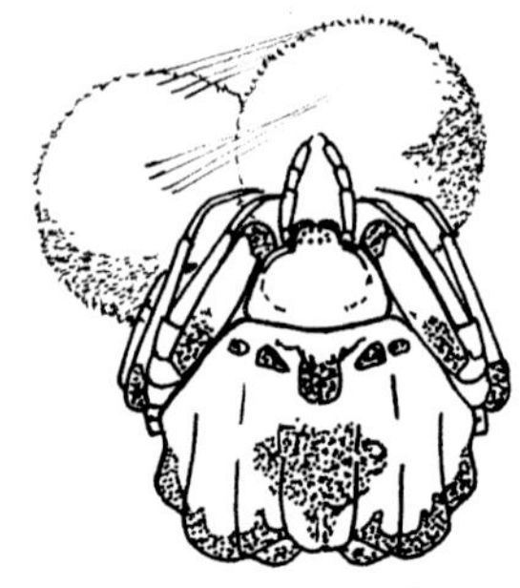

Female Bird-dung *Celaenia*, family Araneidae. Bulky white and brown abdomens mimic bird droppings. Body length 12-20 mm. (p.132)

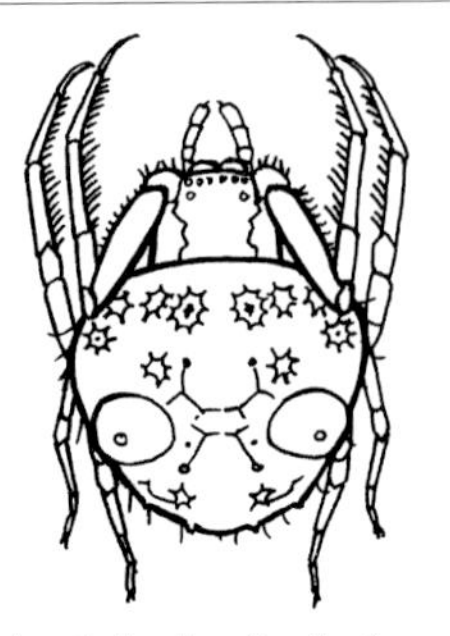

Female Bolas *Ordgarius*, family Araneidae. Yellow-ochre, salmon or cream, brightly coloured nodules and abdominal patterns. Body length 14-24 mm. (p.133)

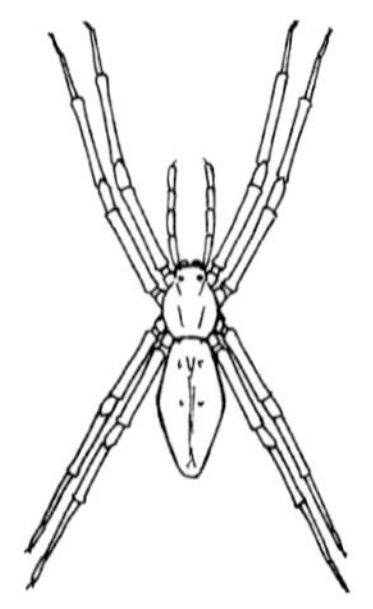

Female Net-casting *Deinopis*, family Deinopidae. Brown to grey, stick-like. Body length 25 mm. (p.135)

Apprentice Weavers (Araneomorphs)

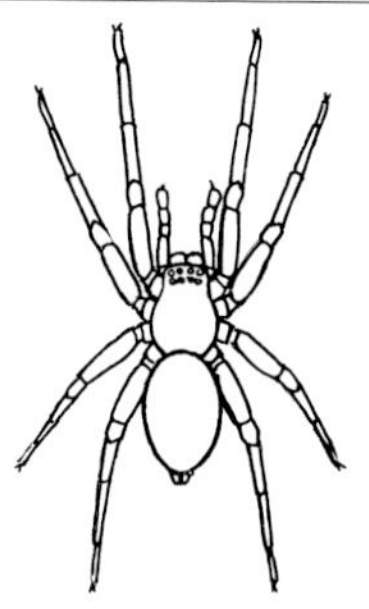

Female Lace-web *Badumna*, family Desidae. Dark-brown, grey or black. Body length 12-18 mm. (p.143)

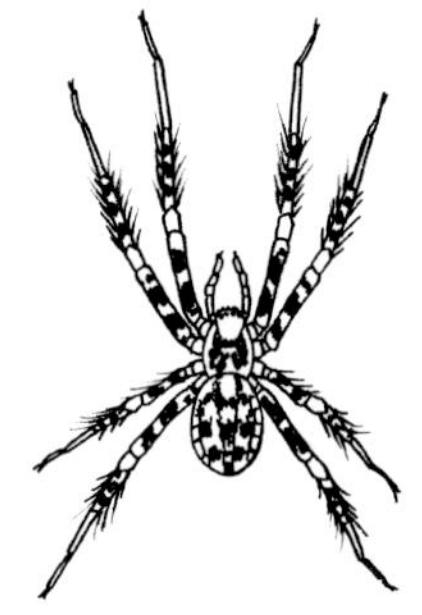

Female Lattice-web *Stiphidium*, family Stiphidiidae. Light brown to yellow ochre, dark brown bands and flecks. Body length 10 mm. (p.145)

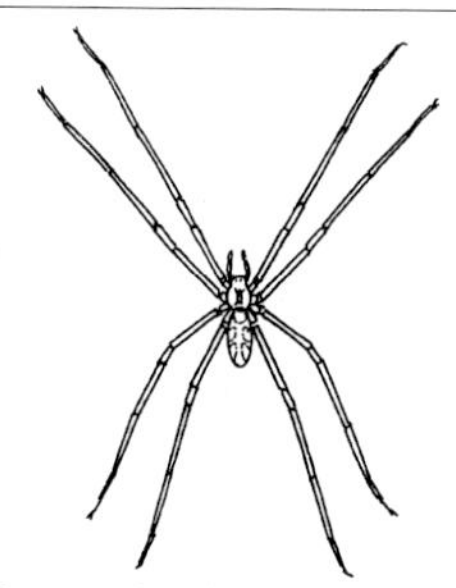

Female Scattered-web *Pholcus*, family Pholcidae. Exceptionally long legs. Body length up to 9 mm. (p.146)

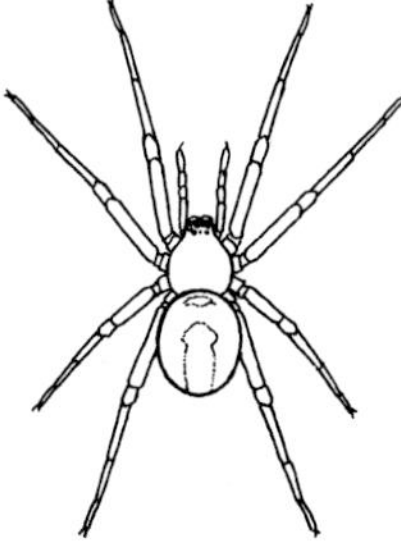

Female Gum-footed-web *Latrodectus*, family Theridiidae. Round abdomen, moderately long legs, tiny fangs. Usually dark, bright spots or stripes on abdomen. Body length 10-14 mm. (p.147)

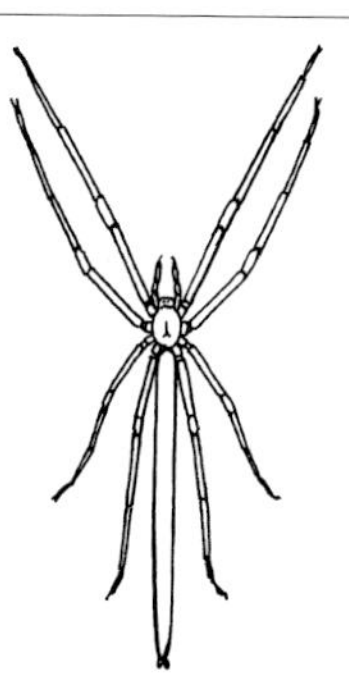

Female Single-thread-trap *Argyrodes*, family Theridiidae. Elongated abdomen, light brown. Body length 20 mm. (p.142)

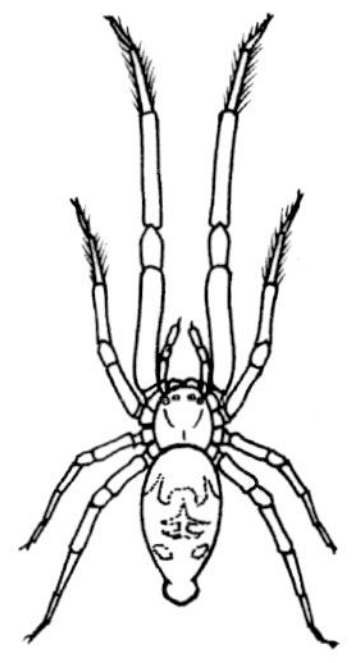

Female Unrefined-wheel-web (Feather-footed) *Uloborus*, family Uloboridae. Grey to fawn. Body length 8-10 mm. (p.148)

Master Weavers (Araneomorphs)

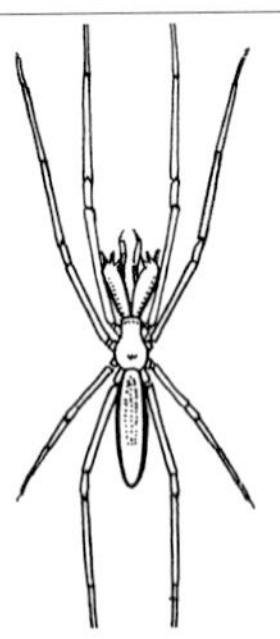

Female Four-jawed *Tetragnatha*, family Tetragnathidae. Huge chelicerae, very long legs, elongated body (length 12 mm). (p.151)

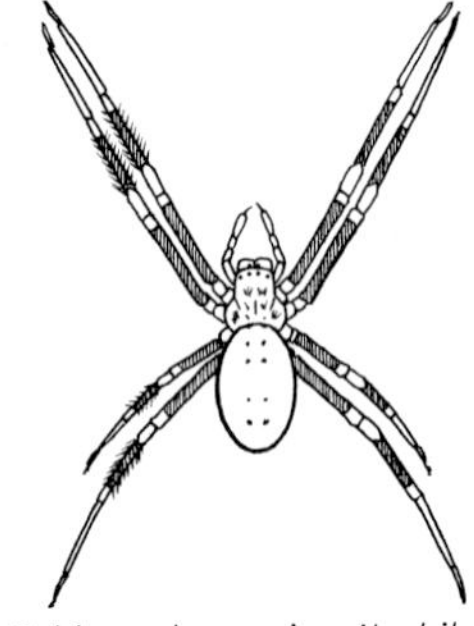

Female Golden-orb-weaving *Nephila*, family Araneidae. Large, with colourful banded legs, silver-grey body 12-45 mm long. (p.153)

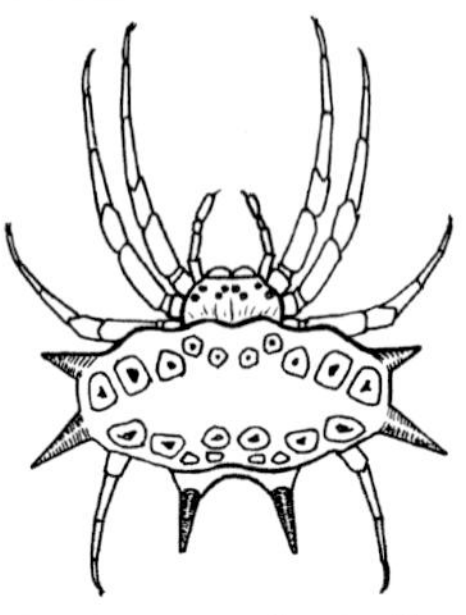

Female Spiny *Gasteracantha*, family Araneidae. Brightly coloured, with spiny abdomen, short legs. Body length 6-10 mm. (p.157)

Female St Andrews Cross *Argiope*, family Araneidae. Banded legs, colourful body 12-15 mm. (p.155)

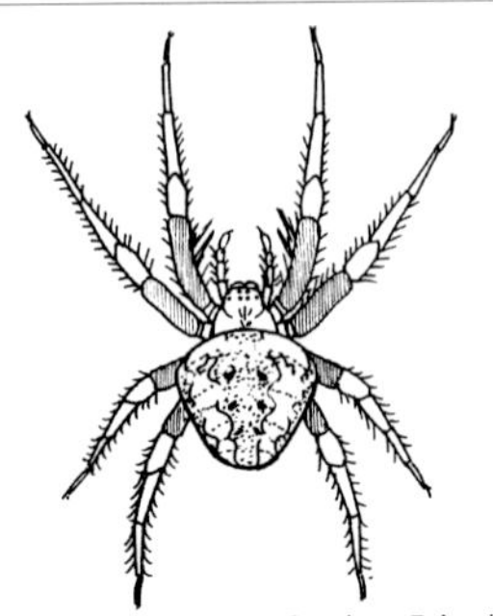

Female Wheel-weaving Garden *Eriophora*, family Araneidae. Colours change to match surroundings. Body length 15-30 mm. (p.158)

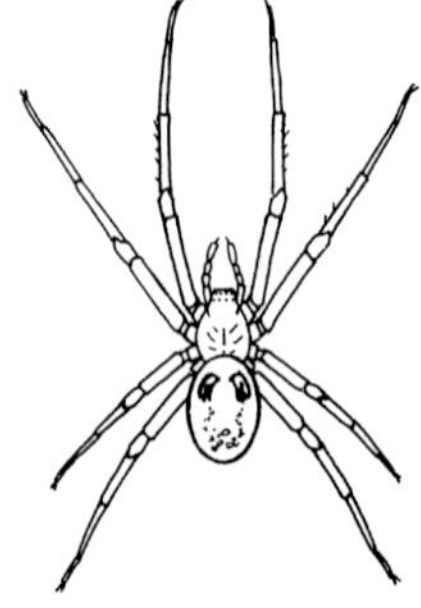

Female Leaf-curling *Phonognatha*, family Araneidae. Colourful abdominal patterns, red-brown limbs. Body length 10-15 mm. (p.161)

MOUSE	*Eastern Mouse Spider* *Missulena bradleyi*

Highly venomous; the bite can cause local swelling, burning and itchiness. The female, a timid, sluggish creature, rarely displays aggression but the colourful male shows aggression and bites if threatened or cornered.

Mouse (male)

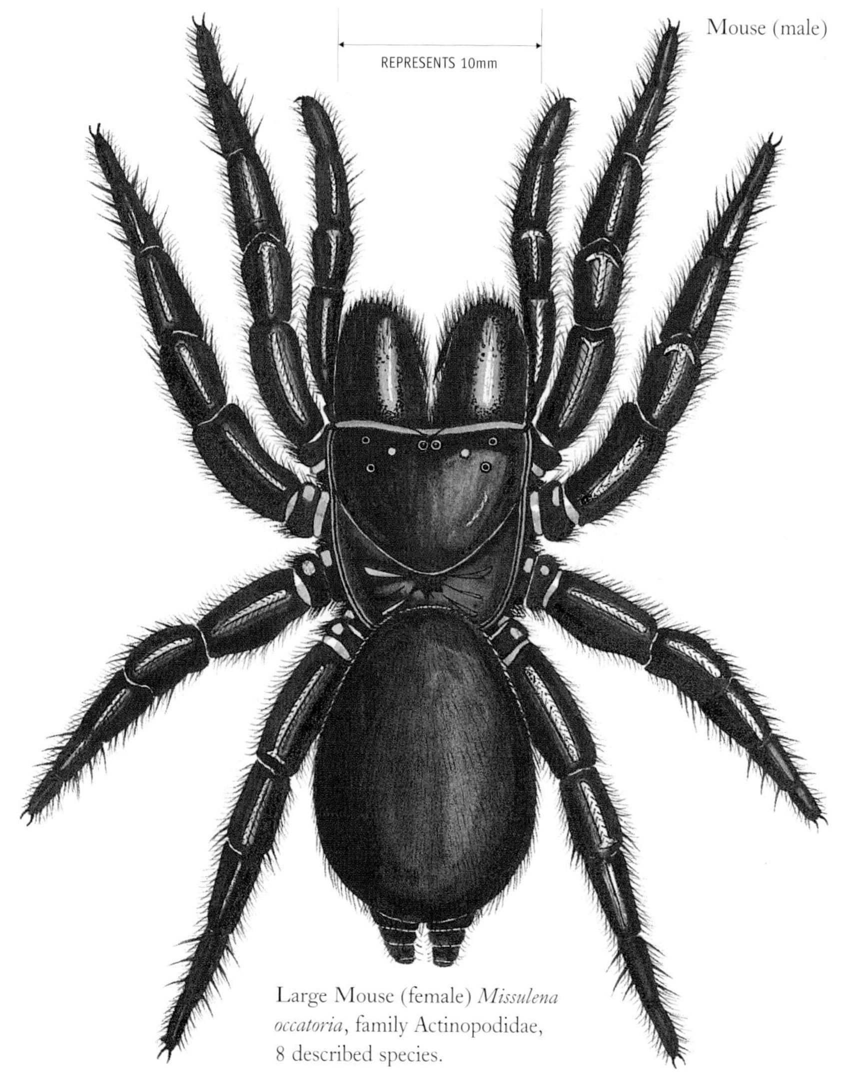

Large Mouse (female) *Missulena occatoria*, family Actinopodidae, 8 described species.

RED-HEADED MOUSE *Missulena occatoria*

Highly venomous; bite can cause local swelling, burning and itchiness. The highly colourful male bites if cornered or handled.

REPRESENTS 8mm

Large Red-headed Mouse (male)
Missulena occatoria,
family Actinopodidae,
8 descr. spp.

NORTHERN TREE FUNNEL-WEB	*Hadronyche formidabilis*

Potentially lethal, particularly to children.

Typical homesite of *Hadronyche formidabilis*

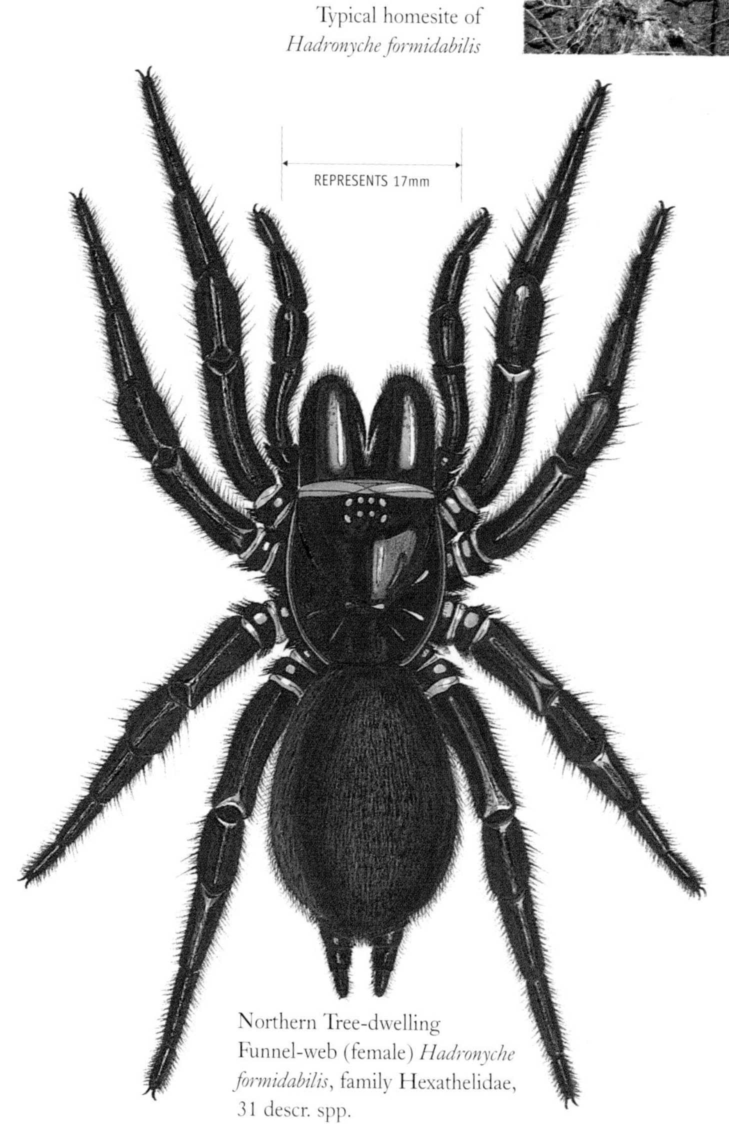

Northern Tree-dwelling Funnel-web (female) *Hadronyche formidabilis*, family Hexathelidae, 31 descr. spp.

SYDNEY FUNNEL-WEB *Atrax robustus*

Highly venomous, deadly. Both the male and female carry atraxotoxin, one of the most dangerous of all toxins found in the animal kingdom.

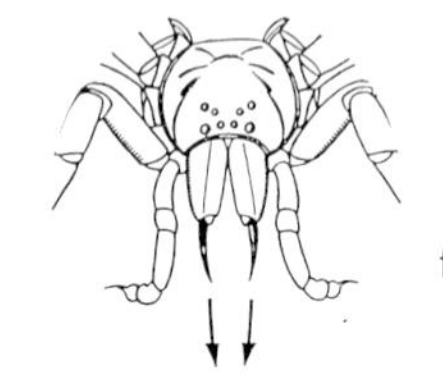

fang action

REPRESENTS 8mm

Sydney Funnel-web (male)
Atrax robustus,
family Hexathelidae,
31 descr. spp.

BLUE MOUNTAINS FUNNEL-WEB *Hadronyche versutus*

Highly venomous. Female spiders of the genera *Hadronyche* and *Atrax* (see illustration) are similar in size, colouring and appearance, but all *Hadronyche* have a highly raised head region, whereas *Atrax* do not. Further, unlike the males of *Atrax robustus*, males of *Hadronyche* have no spurs on the tibia of their second pair of legs.

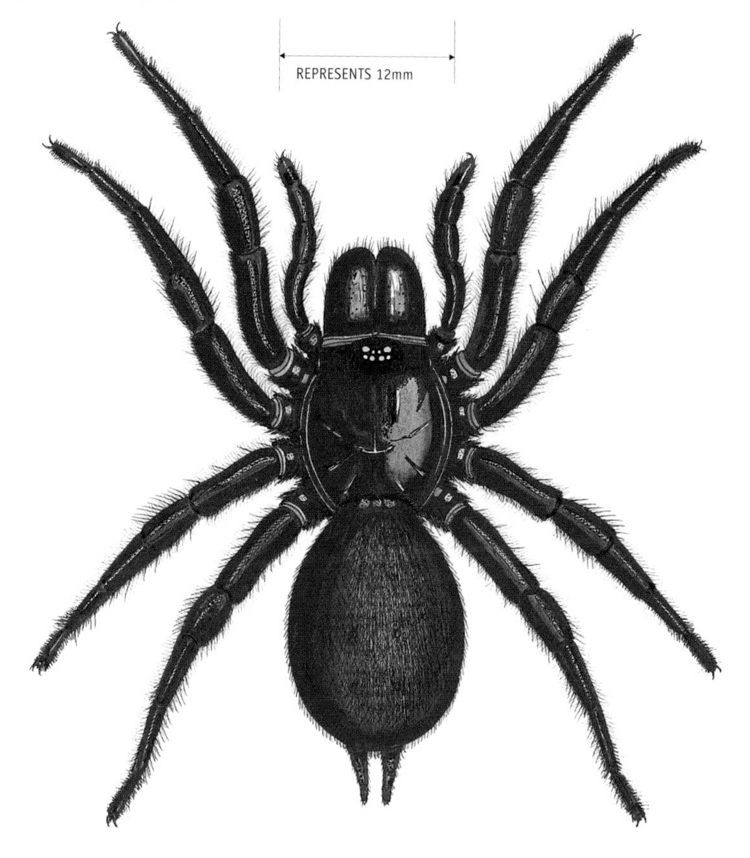

Sydney Funnel-web (female)
Atrax robustus,
family Hexathelidae,
31 descr. spp.

SPECKLED BADGE HUNTSMAN | *Neosparassus calligaster* (formerly *Olios*)

Not lethal but its bite can cause local swelling, burning and itchiness.

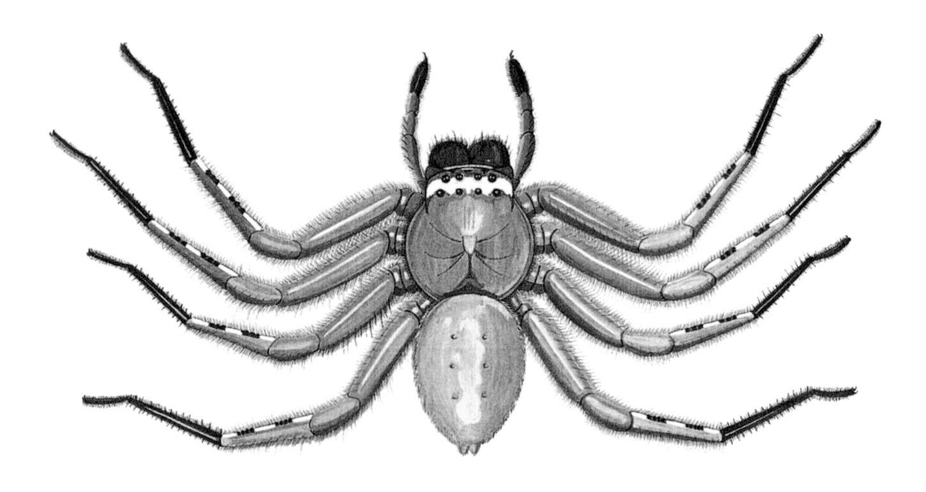

Badge Huntsman (female)
Neosparassus calligaster,
family Heteropodidae,
94 descr. spp.

BROWN BADGE HUNTSMAN *Neosparassus punctatus* (formerly *Olios*)

This species and *N. calligaster* are the only Huntsmans known to cause inconvenience to humans. The bite of *N. punctatus* is the most severe of the two; not lethal, but can cause systemic symptoms—headache, vomiting, nausea, diarrhoea, muscular pains, chills.

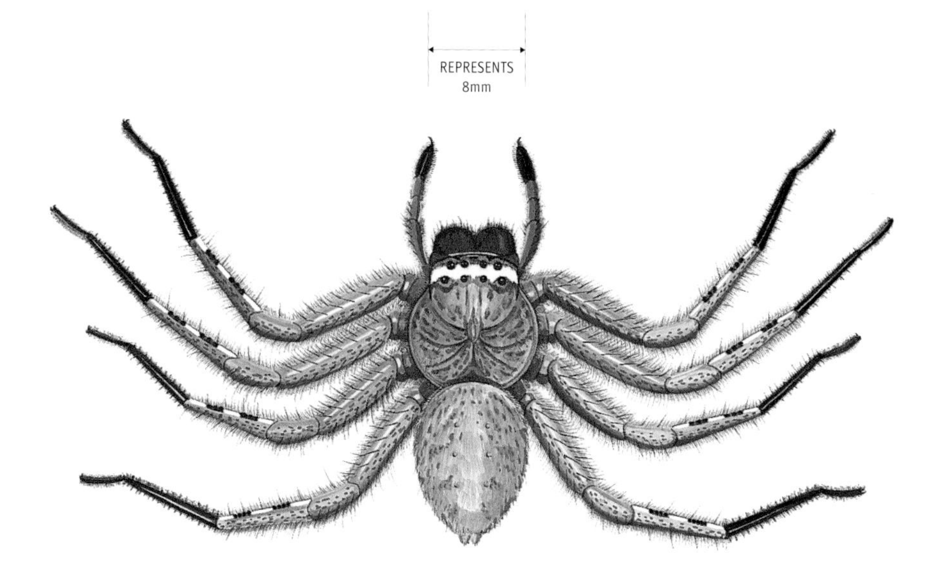

Badge Huntsman (female)
Neosparassus punctatus,
family Heteropodidae,
94 descr. spp.

LARGE SAC

Miturga
(several species)

All spiders in the Miturgidae family have stout fang bases and can give painful bites which may cause systemic symptoms—headache, vomiting, nausea, diarrhoea, muscular pains, chills.

Large Sac (female)
Miturga agelenina,
family Miturgidae,
20 descr. spp.

BIG-JAWED SAC	*Cheiracanthium* spp.

Not lethal but can cause systemic symptoms such as headache, nausea, muscular pain.

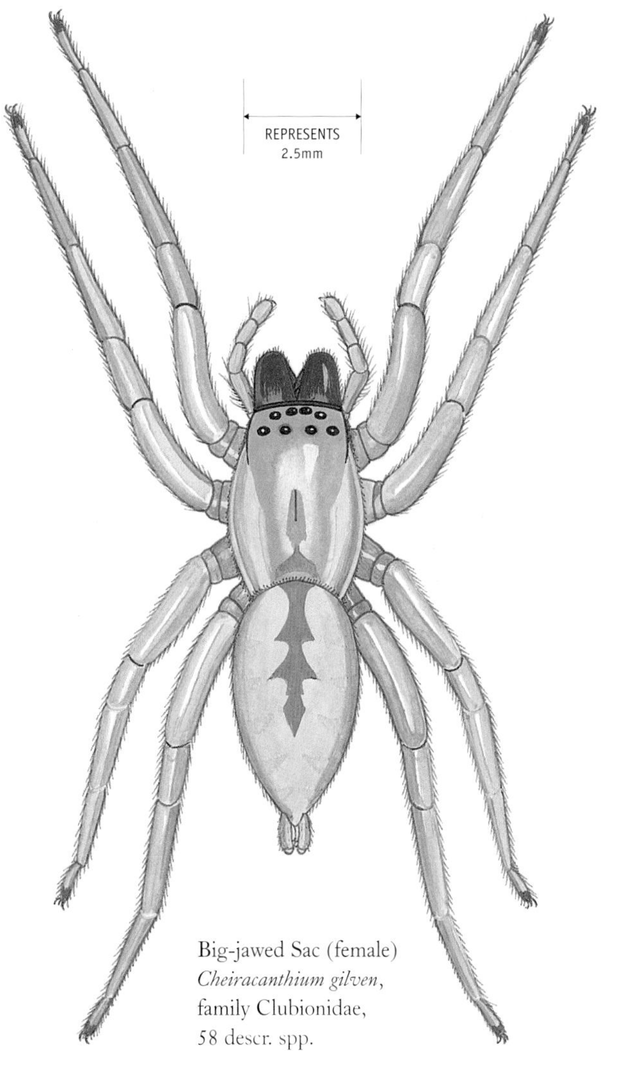

Big-jawed Sac (female)
Cheiracanthium gilven,
family Clubionidae,
58 descr. spp.

WHITE-TAILED *Lampona cylindrata*

Not lethal but can cause systemic symptoms such as headache, vomiting, nausea, diarrhoea, muscular pains, chills. Its venom contains flesh-dissolving enzymes suspected of causing necrotic sores in some cases—'necrosis' means 'death of tissue'.

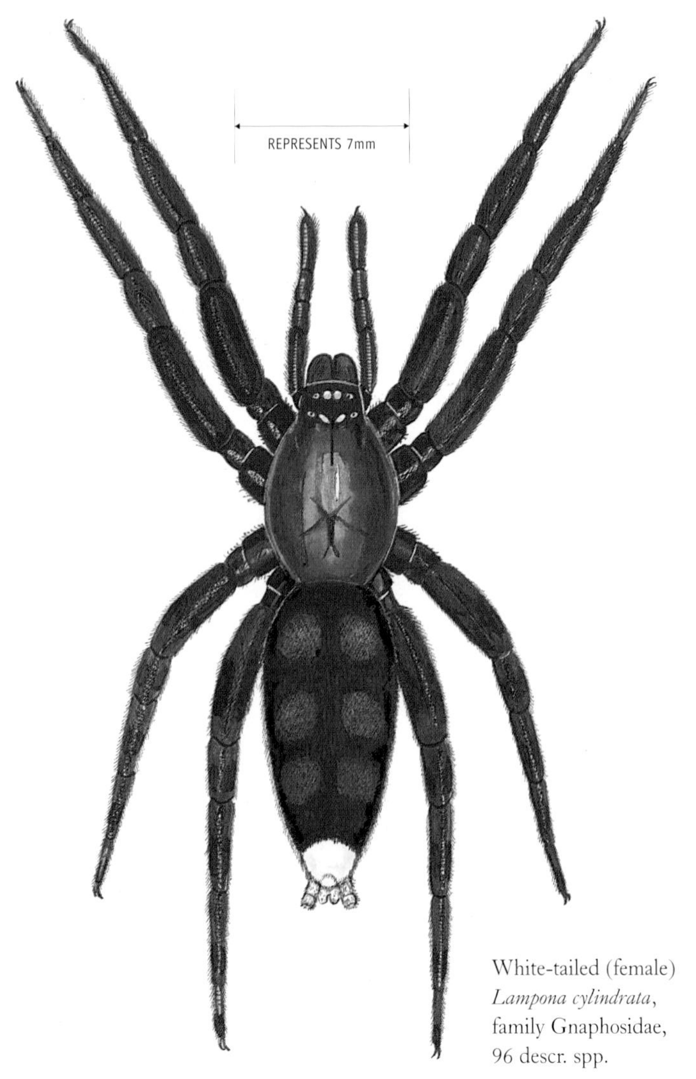

White-tailed (female)
Lampona cylindrata,
family Gnaphosidae,
96 descr. spp.

DYSDERID (introduced spp.)

Dysdera crocota

Can cause considerable pain and swelling at the site of the bite; can also produce slow-healing ulcers. No deaths recorded.

Typical homesite of *Dysdera crocota*

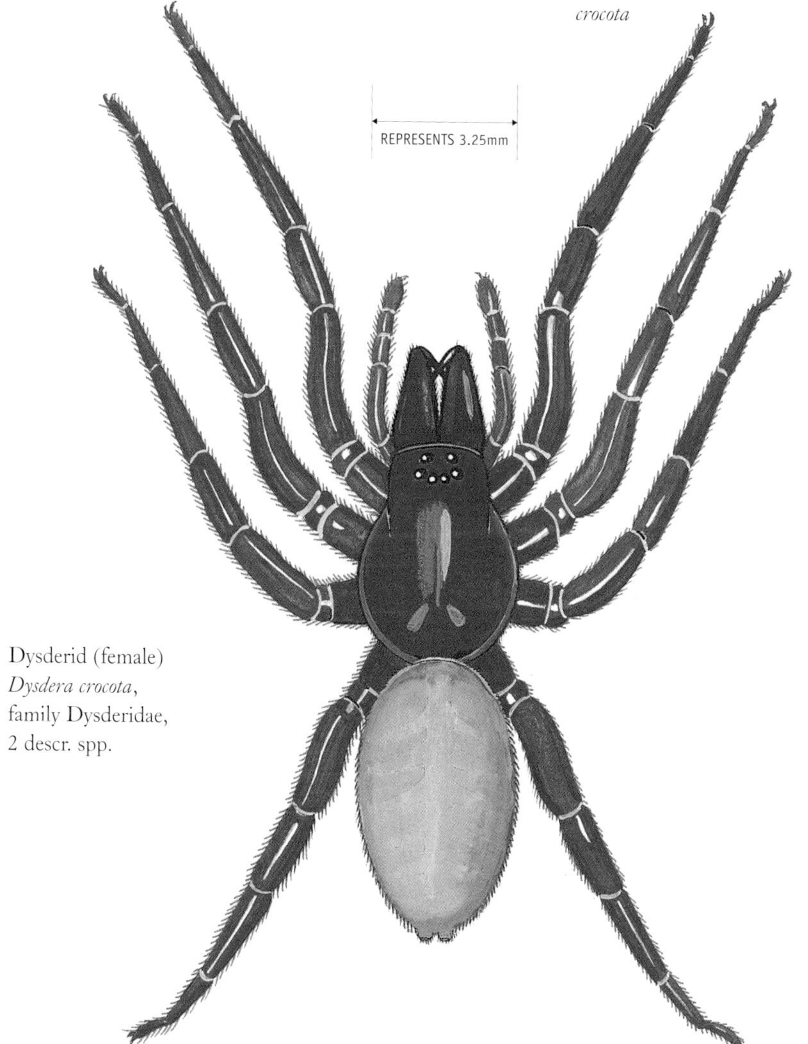

Dysderid (female) *Dysdera crocota*, family Dysderidae, 2 descr. spp.

GARDEN WOLF *Lycosa godeffroyi*

Not an aggressive spider, but should be treated with caution. If handled or molested it can inflict a painful bite which may cause infection and skin lesions to some people. No deaths have been attributed to its bite.

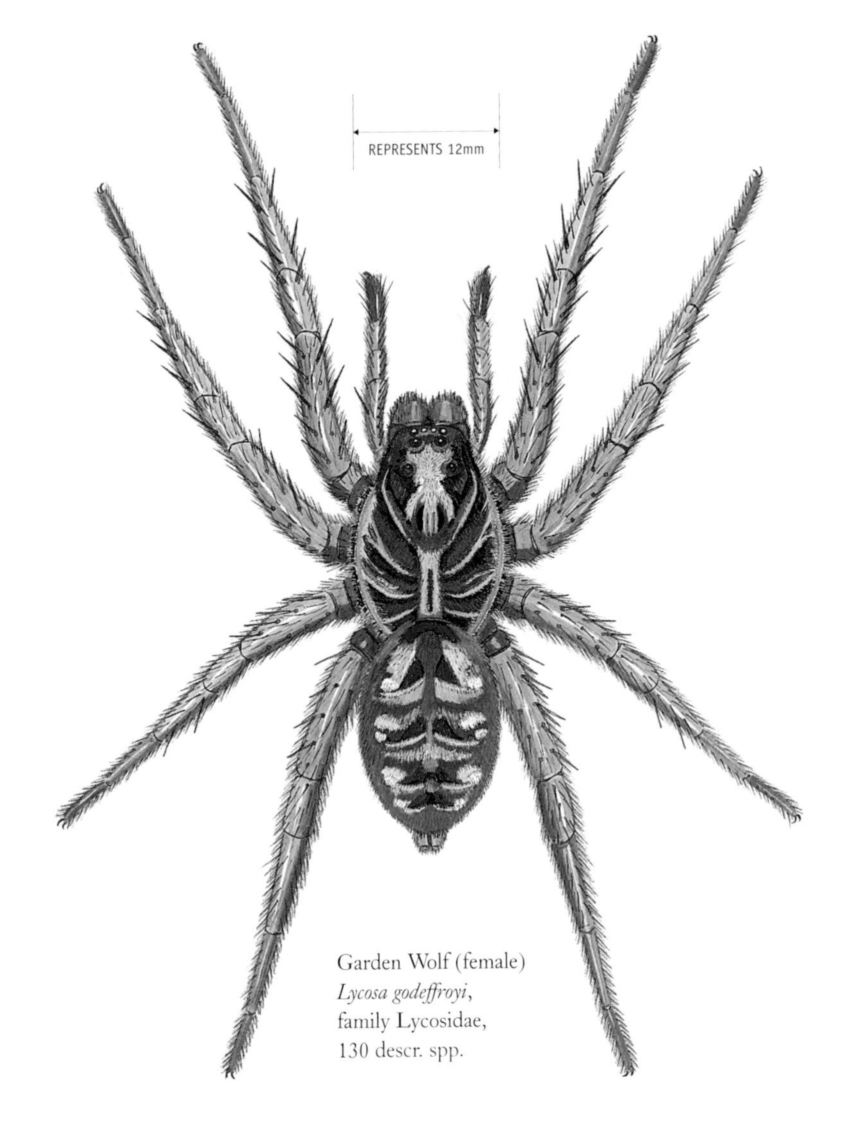

Garden Wolf (female)
Lycosa godeffroyi,
family Lycosidae,
130 descr. spp.

FIDDLE-BACK (introduced species)

Loxosceles laeta and *L. rufescens*

Not an aggressive spider but is potentially dangerous—its bite is considered to be highly venomous.
It can also produce a slow-healing ulcerous sore.

Typical homesite of *Loxosceles laeta* and *L. rufescens*

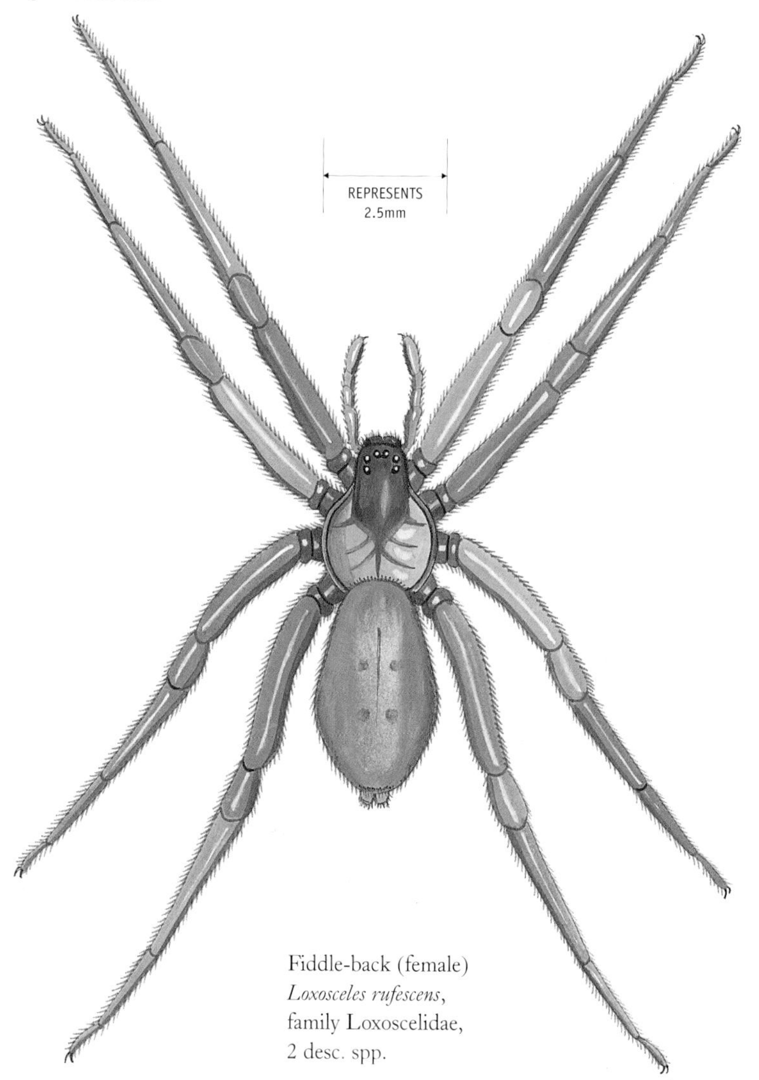

Fiddle-back (female)
Loxosceles rufescens,
family Loxoscelidae,
2 desc. spp.

NORTHERN GREEN JUMPING	*Mopsus mormon*

Not lethal but the bite can inflict headaches, vomiting, nausea, diarrhoea, muscular pains and chills, and is also suspected of causing necrotic sores.

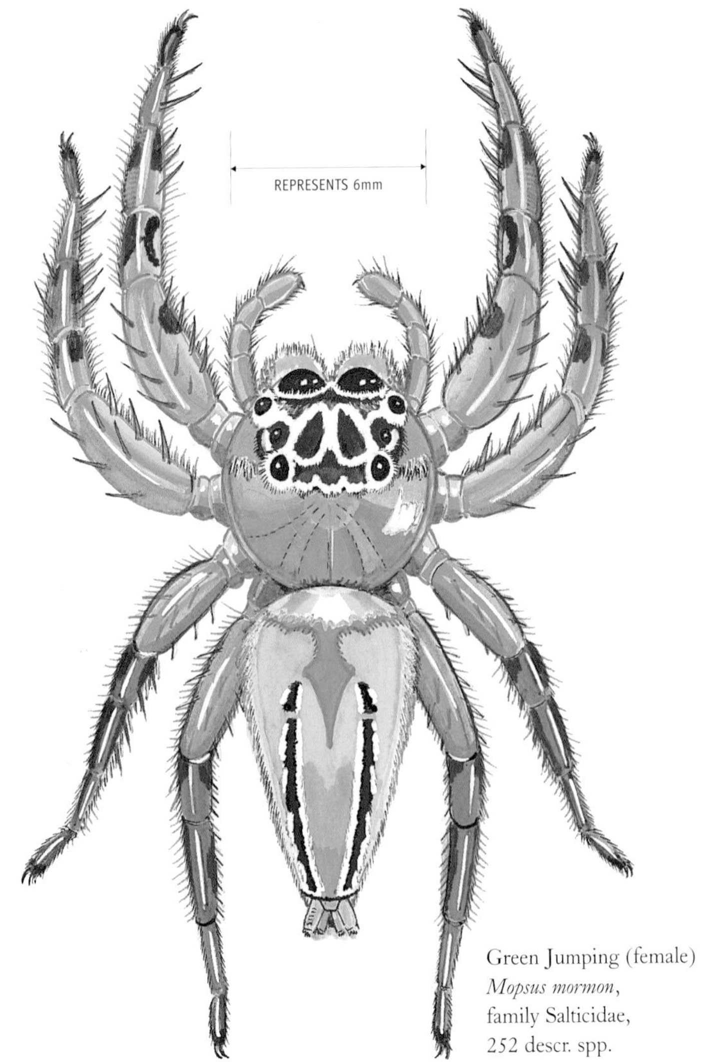

Green Jumping (female)
Mopsus mormon,
family Salticidae,
252 descr. spp.

LARGE BLACK HOUSE *Badumna insignis*

Not lethal but can cause headaches, vomiting, nausea, diarrhoea, muscular pains, chills.

Large Black House (female)
Badumna insignis,
family Desidae,
48 descr. spp.

SMALL BLACK HOUSE *Badumna longinqua*

Not lethal but can cause headaches, vomiting, nausea, diarrhoea, muscular pains, chills.

Small Black House (female)
Badumna longinqua,
family Desidae,
48 descr. spp.

RED-BACK *Latrodectus hasselti*

Not an aggressive spider but the female's venom has proved fatal; the male's fangs are too small to penetrate human skin.

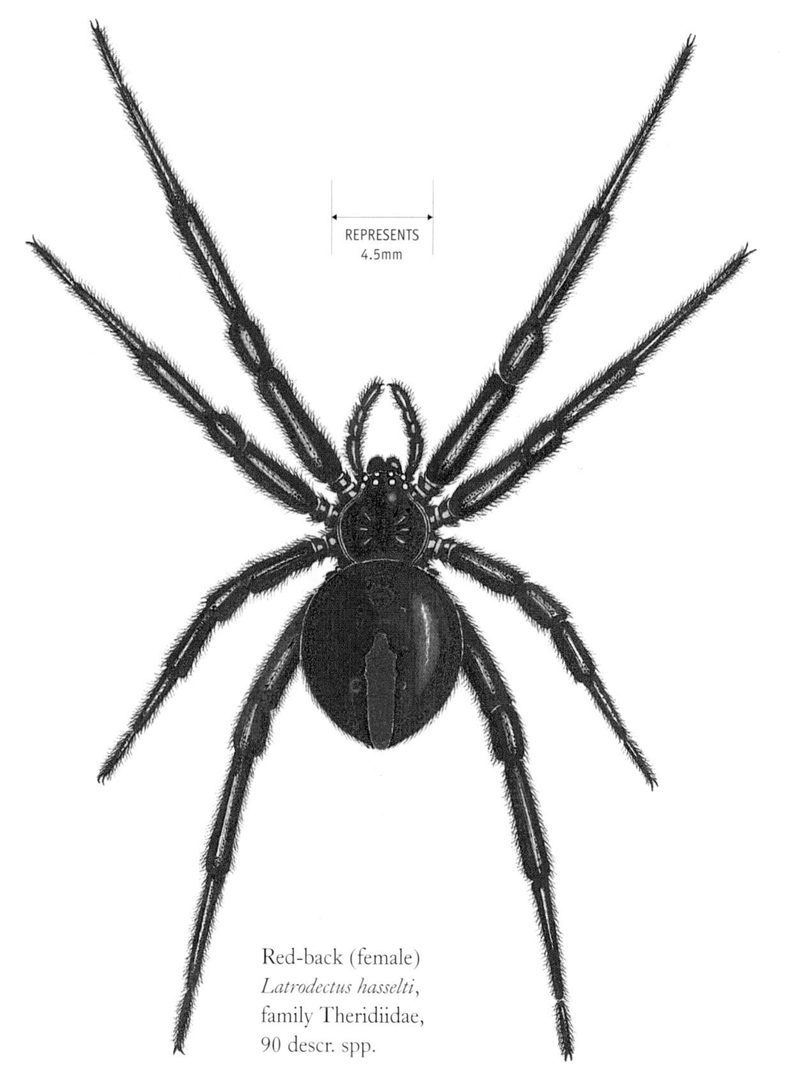

Red-back (female)
Latrodectus hasselti,
family Theridiidae,
90 descr. spp.

FIRST AID FOR SPIDER BITES

A female Blue Mountains Funnel-web, *Hadronyche versutus*.

The venom that spiders use to immobilise and digest prey is not necessarily poisonous to warm-blooded animals, including humans. Certain species can cause death by introducing an extremely toxic substance into the bloodstream; however, the bites of the vast majority of species cause no more inconvenience than a local swelling or pain which passes quickly.

Since this book is a field guide, a brief outline of spider bites and treatment may be useful.

SYMPTOMS OF FUNNEL-WEB BITE

1 The fang action produces two clearly visible puncture marks.
2 Pain and numbness usually occur at the site of the bite within 10 minutes.
3 Nausea and vomiting follow.
4 Profuse perspiring and fainting occur.
5 The victim salivates excessively, frothing at the mouth.
6 Breathing difficulties may turn the victim blue.
7 Cramps and pain spread through the body.
8 The victim may become delirious.
9 There may be violent twitching and contractions of facial and limb muscles; relexes may slow down; eyes may not respond to light.
10 The victim may then lapse into a coma. The secretion of excess fluids into the lungs, and failure of muscles used for breathing are the most likely cause of death.

TREATMENT FOR FUNNEL-WEB BITE

Now that antivenom for this bite is available Australia-wide, full recovery is almost certain; note, too, that envenomation does not always occur with the bite. However, treatment at the nearest hospital should always be sought promptly.

1 Keep the patient as still and calm as possible.
2 Do *not* remove clothing from the wound—roll, push or cut it away.
3 Do *not* elevate the bitten area.
4 Do *not* squeeze, rub, suck or slash open the wound—any such action will only spread the venom more quickly into the bloodstream.

5 Apply a crepe bandage as tightly as you would for a sprain, and extend it the entire length of the limb if possible. If you have no bandage, tear strips from a shirt, dress etc.
6 Attach a splint of any rigid material (e.g. a branch) to immobilise the limb. This can help the body to break down the venom.
7 Do *not* give the patient any fluids or stimulants.
8 Keep the patient warm—this can help to reduce pain.
9 Take the patient to hospital promptly, but without panic, and if possible take along the spider too, for identification.

For a bite to the trunk of the body, apply firm pressure to the wound with crepe bandage and seek antivenom treatment as fast as possible. (A bite to the neck or head cannot be treated with first-aid.)

Note: Do *not* use the pressure-immobilisation method for any other spider bite—it should be used only for a Funnel-web bite. Most important, apply the bandage as fast as possible. The effects of a Funnel-web bite wear off after a few hours of being vaccinated.

SYMPTOMS OF RED-BACK (*Latrodectus hasselti*) BITE

Before an effective antivenom was developed in 1956, 12 people in Australia were reported to have died from this bite; no-one has died from it since.

1 The bite produces a clearly visible puncture mark.
2 The venom is normally very slow to act, and the first symptom (usually apparent within an hour) is a slight stinging sensation at the site of the bite.
3 If not treated promptly the patient may experience swelling and tenderness around the puncture, and a white patch may form, with local pain (the extent of this varies with each case).
4 After some hours, stiffness around the infected area may occur.
5 Absorption of the venom in the lymphatic system can cause the patient intense pain in the lower limbs.
6 Intense shivering may follow, with profuse perspiring of the bitten area but the rest of the body remaining dry. *This symptom occurs only with a Red-back bite.*
7 Sometimes paralysis of the lower limbs occurs.

TREATMENT FOR RED-BACK BITE

An antivenom is available in all major hospitals Australia-wide. If the bite occurs far from any hospital, proceed as follows.

1 Do not panic. The effects of a bite can take hours, even days, to take effect, so there is ample time to reach a hospital for antivenom

treatment—of course, the sooner the treatment the better.

2 Keep the patient as still and calm as possible.
3 Remove any tight clothing and make the patient as warm and comfortable as possible.
4 Do *not* elevate the bitten area; do *not* squeeze, rub, slash open or suck at the wound—all these actions will spread the toxin.
5 Do *not* give the patient any fluids.
6 Do *not* apply restrictive bandages to a Red-back bite. The amount of venom injected by this spider is tiny and moves very slowly; restriction only causes more pain.
7 Ice can alleviate pain, but do not apply it directly to the skin—wrap it in a towel.

SYMPTOMS OF WHITE-TAILED (Lampona cylindrata) BITE

This species is, of all Australian spiders, suspected as the chief cause of necrosis (death of tissue). This nocturnal Open Range Hunter of the Sac group occurs throughout Australia and has adapted to living in houses, especially bedrooms and bathrooms.

1 The bite produces a clearly visible puncture mark.
2 The bite can cause a burning local pain, sometimes followed by blistering and ulceration; however, the symptoms have no predictable pattern.
3 The speed of tissue damage and of other symptoms varies widely. Ulceration may begin with surface blistering or with a darkening of the flesh beneath the bite.
4 Reaction can be either rapid and painful, with violent vomiting and diarrhoea, or gradual with relatively little pain.
5 If necrosis spreads extensively, the only way to retard the damage is to remove the dead tissue and scrape around it. The wound may require skin graft. In some cases toes and fingers have required amputation, but skin grafting has been completely successful in other cases. It is thought that the skin is consumed by a digestive enzyme that liquefies the internal tissues of the spider's prey, and it is also thought that in some way this digestive enzyme can renew itself.

FIRST-AID TREATMENT FOR WHITE-TAILED BITE

Although dangerous, the bite is not fatal. An amino acid L-Cysteine ointment can counteract the necrotic effect of the venom. I have also found that aloe vera in ointment or fresh leaf form can also greatly help to neutralise the effects of the bite; apply it generously over the wound three or four times a day until it heals.

The portion of flesh-dissolving enzymes contained in the venom of a single bite would fit on the head of a pin. The venom carries the bacterium *Mycobacterium ulcerans*, the microscopic organism that is believed to cause the spread of an infected, ulcerous sore.

CLASSIFYING SPIDERS

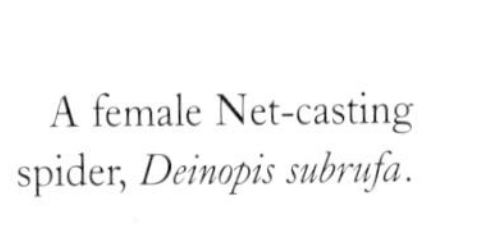

A female Net-casting spider, *Deinopis subrufa*.

Australia is host to a large and varied spider fauna. The more research achieved, the more species uncovered. It's not that many of the undescribed spiders have not been seen before, but they have previously been grouped with other species and not given their rightful status in relationship to the environment. Australia is indeed fortunate in still having large regions of land that retain a natural environment for supporting our unique flora and fauna. It is the heartfelt hope of all people that these 'islands' will continue to support the vitally important occupants.

This handbook will prove useful for the seasoned spider-watcher and the beginner alike and is intended to give a well-rounded profile of the species more commonly found in Australia. Certain species are included either because they are typical of their genera or family or because they are common. The most common spiders represent about 10 per cent of Australia's species. Whether we are at home or in the bushland, it is important to be able to distinguish the potentially dangerous spiders from those that are completely harmless to humans in order to eliminate unnecessary panic, which can cause accidents. By being able to positively identify a poisonous species, should a bite ever occur, the correct first-aid measures and medical attention (including any necessary antivenom) can be administered without delay.

A certain mystery and intrigue accompanies the lives of spiders mainly because of their nocturnal activities, poisonous properties and their marvellous silken webs that are specifically designed and constructed to capture prey. Spiders continue to fascinate people of all cultures. Even though some spiders are grotesque by certain standards, others are strikingly beautiful in their form and colouring and so are the silken creations they build with engineering ingenuity. Spiders do not eat our food crops, nor do they carry or spread disease.

Because much of the natural habitat has been destroyed in many urban and rural districts, the number of spiders as well as the number of species has greatly declined. The indiscriminate use of pesticides kills both friends and foes. In addition, introduced animals (e.g. rabbits, sheep and cattle) have caused soil erosion and continue to denude vast tracts of land once covered with woodlands, shrubs and grasses. The regeneration of the remaining pockets of native trees is under continual threat. Young regrowth is quickly eaten by grazing animals and when the older established trees do finally die, they will not have been replaced. Such vegetation offers micro habitats to all manner of smaller creatures, including the spiders.

The classification of all lifeforms is based on scientifically organising the types of animals and plants into groups, each a subset of the one before. This science is called taxonomy and is based on the study of the classifications of organisms. By thoroughly examining the morphological features of any animal or plant, the taxonomist is able to determine where an organism 'best fits' in relation to other similar organisms. Evolutionary descent is the cornerstone to this study and when an organism is correctly classified, it should be possible to place it in its proper relationship to other lifeforms. Nevertheless, the classification of spiders remains controversial at this stage. Although 2,000 Australian species have been described, thousands more are still awaiting description. Luck, skill and diligence will reveal these, hopefully in time to help us understand a good deal more about their diversity and their relationship to the environment.

To give an example of how this classification works, let us look at the common Wheel-weaving Garden spider: this is its common name and sometimes you will find that the very same spider has been given a different common name. To avoid this confusion, it is given a scientific name (universally applied)—in this case, *Eriophora transmarina*. The full classification of the spider is as follows:

Phylum	Arthropoda;
Class	Arachnida;
Order	Araneae;
Suborder	Araneomorphae;
Family	Araneidae;
Genus	*Eriophora*;
Species	*transmarina*.

As you see we have used only the last two names, *Eriophora transmarina*, in describing the Wheel-weaving Garden Spider. The phylum, class, order, suborder and family names indicate the spider's evolutionary relationships. The species name is the most specific (although some organisms are divided still further into subspecies) and it must be prefaced by the name of the genus to which that species belongs. The genus and the species names are always Latin names written in italic. The genus name always begins with an upper case letter and the species name is all lower case.

Even among expert araneologists, opinions differ over the appropriate placing of certain spiders. Sometimes a species has to be removed from one place and put in another because a closer relationship is discovered. When a species is removed from its original genus, the name of the author who originally described and placed that species always follows: e.g. *Eriophora transmarina* (Keyserling 1865).

AUSTRALIA'S FAMILIES OF SPIDERS

MYGALOMORPHAE—PRIMITIVE SPIDERS

In Australia the Mygalomorphs or Primitive spiders consist of 10 families and 241 described species. The families are: Actinopodidae, Barychelidae, Ctenizidae, Cyrtaucheniidae, Dipluridae, Hexathelidae, Idiopidae, Migidae, Nemisiidae, Theraphosidae. These spiders represent 13% of all Australian spiders.

Mygalomorph (Primitive spider).

HYPOCHILOMORPHAE—THE LIVING LINKS

In Australia only two families from this group are represented: Gradungulidae and Hickmaniidae. They represent only a tiny percentage of Australian spiders.

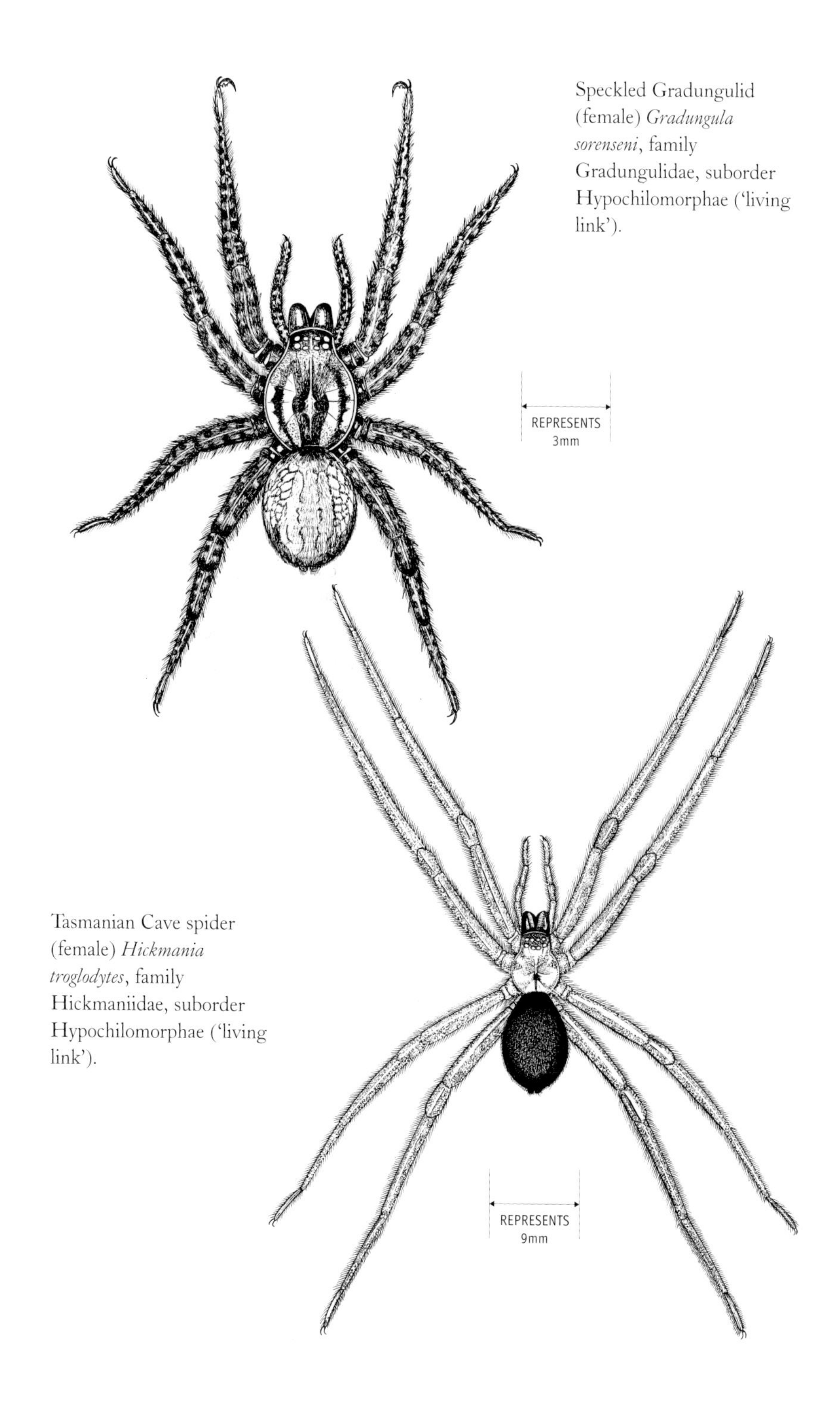

Speckled Gradungulid (female) *Gradungula sorenseni*, family Gradungulidae, suborder Hypochilomorphae ('living link').

Tasmanian Cave spider (female) *Hickmania troglodytes*, family Hickmaniidae, suborder Hypochilomorphae ('living link').

ARANEOMORPHAE—MODERN SPIDERS

Open-range Hunters. The Open-range Hunting group of Araneomorphs consists of 28 families and 853 described species and represents about 45% of Australia's described spiders. These families are: Archaeidae, Clubionidae, Ctenidae, Cycloctenidae, Dysderidae, Gnaphosidae, Hadrotarsidae, Heteropodidae, Holarchaeidae, Loxoscelidae, Lycosidae, Mimetidae, Miturgidae, Oonopidae, Orsolobidae, Oxyopidae, Palpimanidae, Pararchaeidae, Pisauridae, Salticidae, Scytodidae, Segestriidae, Selenopidae, Tetrablemmidae, Textricellidae, Toxopidae, Zodariidae, and Zoridae.

Ambushers and Anglers. The Ambushers and Angler group of Araneomorphs consists of seven families and 200 described species, and represents about 10% of Australia's described spiders. The families are: Araneidae, Cryptothelidae, Deinopidae, Gnaphosidae, Hersiliidae, Thomisidae, Toxopidae. Note: the family Araneidae is also well represented in the Master Weavers group.

Apprentice Weavers. This group consists of 20 families and 270 described species and represents about 14% of Australia's described spiders. The families are: Agelenidae, Amaurobiidae, Amphinectidae, Cyatholipidae, Deinopidae, Desidae, Dictynidae, Dysderidae, Filistatidae, Hahnidae, Linyphiidae, Micropholcommatidae, Nicodamidae, Oecobiidae, Pholcidae, Psechridae, Stiphidiidae, Theridiidae, Theridiosomatidae, Uloboridae.

Master Weavers. This group consists of six families and 340 described species and represents about 17% of Australia's described spiders. The families are: Anapidae, Araneidae, Metidae, Mysmemidae, Symphtytognathidae, and Tetragnathidae.

FIVE LEVELS OF HABITAT

UNDERGROUND (BURROW-ENTRANCE)

Living underground, the females of these spiders are seen only by digging them out. Holes and crevices in rocks, underneath decaying logs or burrows below ground are the permanent homesites for most of the Primitive group of the suborder Mygalomorphae. These are essentially 'wait and grab spiders', relying on crawling insects to blunder or stumble into capture range. They usually stay close to their burrow entrance. Trapdoor spiders commonly inhabit drier situations than Funnel-webs do. Depending on the species, their holes may be quite extensive, and some are lidded. Funnel-webs favour moist, dark undisturbed situations, and construct long silken tubes through litter or into the ground between tree roots or rock piles.

GROUND LEVEL

Rocks under bark, low foliage and waterways are favoured by the Open Range Hunters group—Modern spiders of the suborder Araneomorphae. Most of these spiders are nocturnal and take the initiative in finding prey instead of waiting for it to come to them. For example, the Wolf spiders (family Lycosidae) make burrows in the soil and venture out to hunt for prey at dusk. Huntsman spiders (family Heteropodidae) and Sac spiders (families Clubionidae, Gnaphosidae and Miturgidae) favour crevices in rocks and behind bark, coming out to hunt at night. Jumping spiders (family Salticidae) prefer to hunt on low foliage and tree trunks during daylight and Nursery-web spiders (family Pisauridae) live out their entire lifecycle in and beside streams, ponds and creeks, hunting both day and night.

FLOWERS, SHRUBBERY AND TREE TRUNKS

These spiders position themselves among insect populations where capture is assured. Flowers, shrubbery and tree trunks are favoured by the Ambushers and Anglers group, Modern spiders of the suborder Araneomorphae. Most of these spiders are nocturnal hunters. For example, Crab spiders (family Thomisidae) exploit the insect-attracting properties of flowers to capture prey. Triangular Spiders (family Araneidae) wait on foliage frequented by flying insects. Orchard, Bolas and Bird Dung Mimicking spiders (family Araneidae) position themselves on foliage and tree trunks and use their highly cryptic forms, colouring and sophisticated pheromone attractants to lure prey. The Net-casting spiders (family Deinopidae) construct silken nets which they throw over unsuspecting prey as it moves into netting range.

MEDIUM-HEIGHT FOLIAGE

Tall shrubs, tree stumps, sandstone caves and rock ledges are favoured by spiders that have developed some form of silken snare to capture prey. These spiders form the Apprentice Weavers group, and are Modern spiders of the suborder Araneomorphae. For example, Lace-webs (families Amaurobidae, Desidae, Dictynidae and Oecobiidae) usually build their silken snares among medium foliage and cave walls or cliff faces. Lattice-webs (families Agelenidae, Linyphiidae and Stiphidiidae) build their snares among low to medium foliage, rock ledges and hollow tree stumps. Tangle-webs (families Pholcidae and Theridiidae) build their snares in low to medium foliage, hollow tree stumps, beneath rock ledges and on the walls of sandstone caves. Unrefined Wheel-web spiders (family Uloboridae) build their snares among medium foliage. Flying insects form the bulk of the diet of the Apprentice Weavers group.

LOW TO MEDIUM-HEIGHT FOLIAGE, TALL SHRUBS AND TREES

The spiders building aerial wheel webs construct their magnificent two-dimensional snares between the flight paths of insects, using trees and tall shrubs to support the webs. For example, the Big-jawed spiders (family Tetragnathidae) build horizontal wheel webs above water and tall grass. Golden Orb-weaving, St Andrew's Cross, Wheel-weaving Garden, Spiny, and Leaf-curling spiders (family Araneidae) demonstrate the keenest observation of insect behaviour.

Note: There is one more situation favoured by several spiders—the conditions created by human habitation. At least ten of the world's spider species are referred to as domestic species: the Grey House spider *Achaeranea tepidariorum* (family Theridiidae); two Sac spiders—*Cheiracanthium mordax* (family Clubionidae) and *Dysdera crocota* (family Dysderidae); The Redback *Latrodectus hasselti* (family Theridiidae); two Fiddle-backs—*Loxosceles laeta* and *L. rufescens* (family Loxoscelidae); two Daddy Long-legs—*Pholcus phalangoides* and *P. sphaeroides* (family Pholcidae); the Spitting spider *Scytodes thoracica* (family Scytodidae); and the Cupboard spider *Steatoda livens* (family Theridiidae).

These spiders live in a communal relationship with humans, feeding on the cockroaches, flies, silverfish and moths that scavenge for our food scraps. Equally at home indoors or out are the Red-back, Black House and Huntsman spiders. Just outside our buildings, on porches and verandahs where we have lights, it is common to see members of the Bolas, Crab, Jumping, Net-casting, Orchard, Wolf, Trapdoor, and Wheel-weaving spiders.

ANATOMY AND HOW IT WORKS

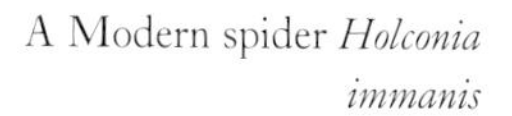

A Modern spider *Holconia immanis*

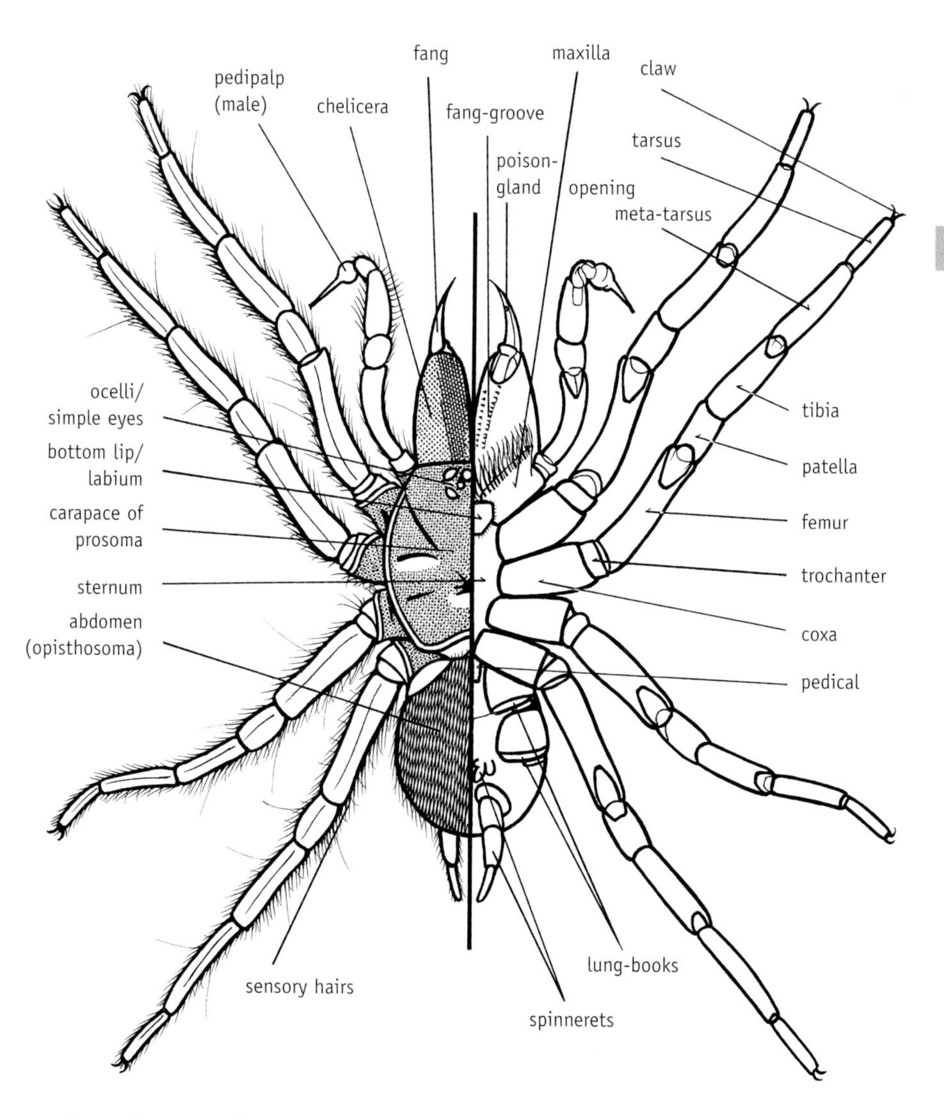

External anatomy of a male Primitive.

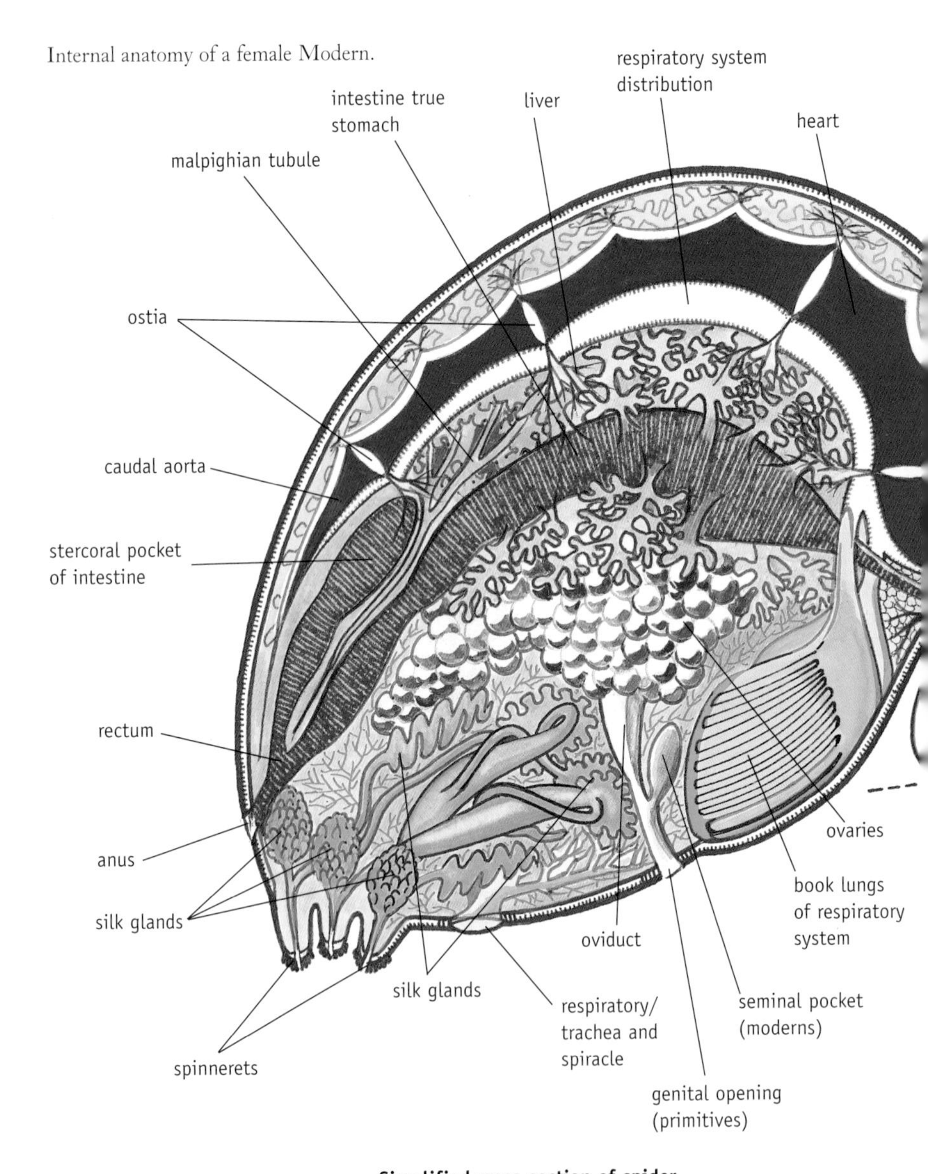

Internal anatomy of a female Modern.

Simplified cross-section of spider

	Circulatory system/heart and blood
	Digestive system/stomachs/liver
	Respiratory system/book-lungs/trachea
	Silk-manufacturing system/silk glands

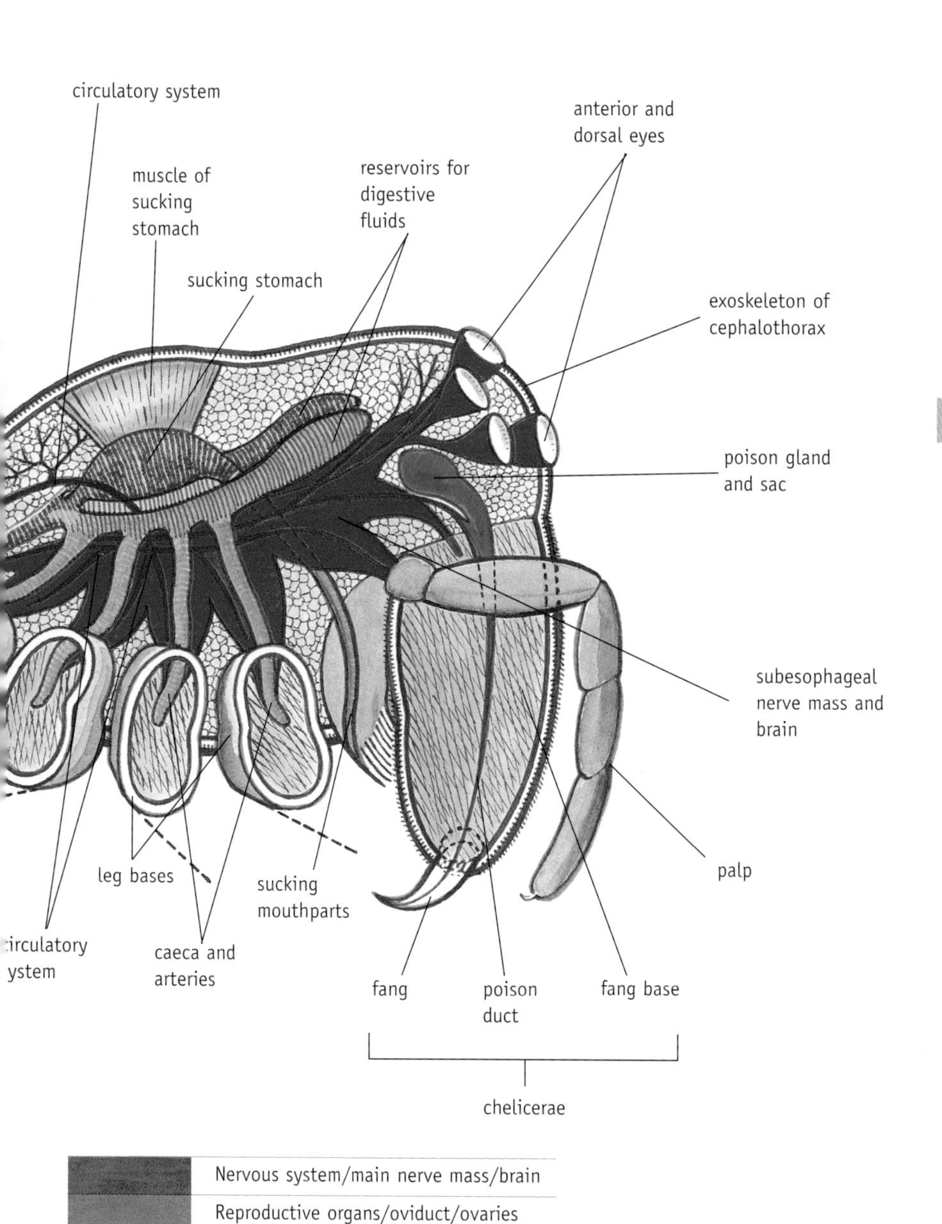
circulatory system
muscle of sucking stomach
reservoirs for digestive fluids
anterior and dorsal eyes
sucking stomach
exoskeleton of cephalothorax
poison gland and sac
subesophageal nerve mass and brain
palp
leg bases
sucking mouthparts
irculatory
ystem
caeca and arteries
fang
poison duct
fang base
chelicerae
Nervous system/main nerve mass/brain
Reproductive organs/oviduct/ovaries
Venom gland/poison-sac/poison duct
Exoskeleton/legs/pedipalp/mouth

Cephalothorax and abdomen of Wolf spider with newly formed egg sac.

The apparent scarcity of material on the biology of Australian spiders, other than that concerning their toxicology and taxonomy, reflects modern society's disregard for the spider's ecological role in our everyday life. Without spiders, the world's insect populations would soar, so that famine and disease would be even more widespread than they already are. To understand spiders and the roles they play, it's necessary to examine their physical make-up.

Basically, a spider's body consists of two major portions resembling a figure of eight. The front part of the cephalothorax (head-on-chest) and the rear part, the abdomen (hind body), are supported on eight legs.

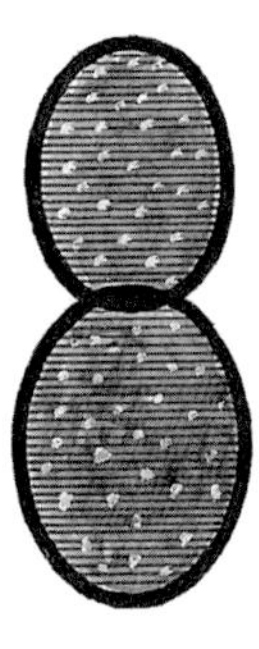

The body has two main sections, like a figure 8.

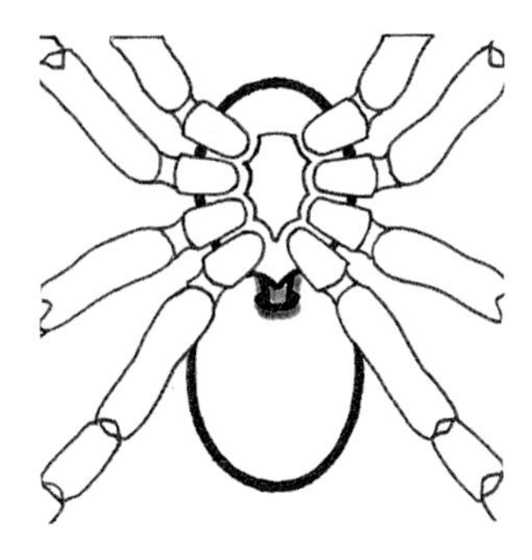

The two main body sections are joined by a pedicel (waist).

CEPHALOTHORAX

The cephalothorax bears the eyes above, and the fangs, mouthparts and leg attachments below. The eight legs are hinged off stout leg-bases called coxa. A stiff shield covers the dorsal surface—the carapace, and the ventral surface—the sternum. The internal organs, including the brain and nervous system, are well protected.

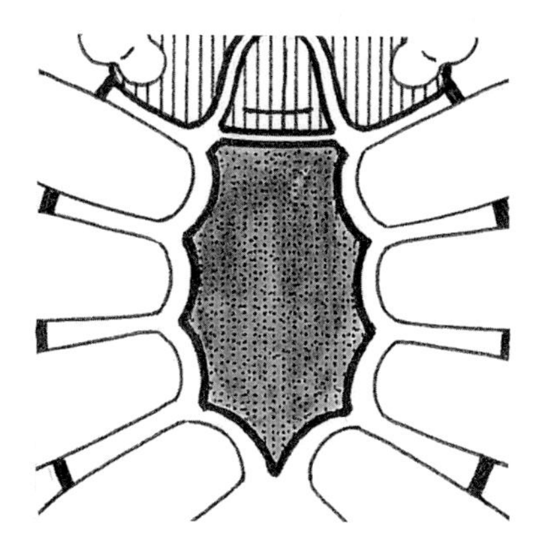

The sternum, a sclerotised plate, protects the ventral surface.

ABDOMEN

The abdomen is usually the most vulnerable portion of the spider's body. It houses the circulatory, digestive, respiratory, reproductive and silk-manufacturing systems. On the ventral surface of the abdomen are two, three or four patches which indicate the position of the book-lungs lying directly beneath the cuticle. These book-lungs supply oxygen to all parts of the body including appendages. Mygalomorphs (Primitive spiders)

Book-lungs of Badge Huntsman (Heteropodidae).

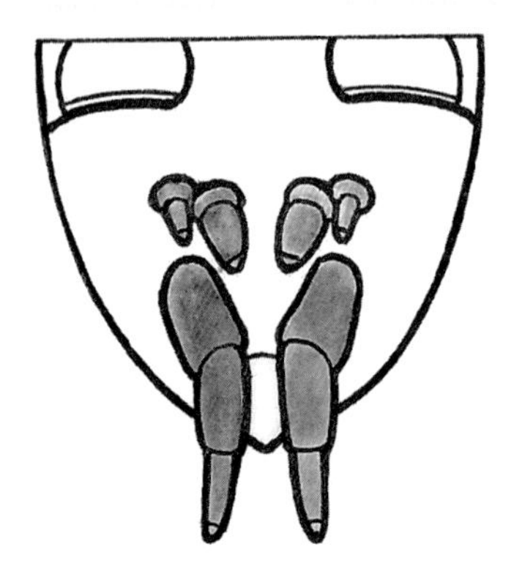

Primitive spiders do not have a cribellum.

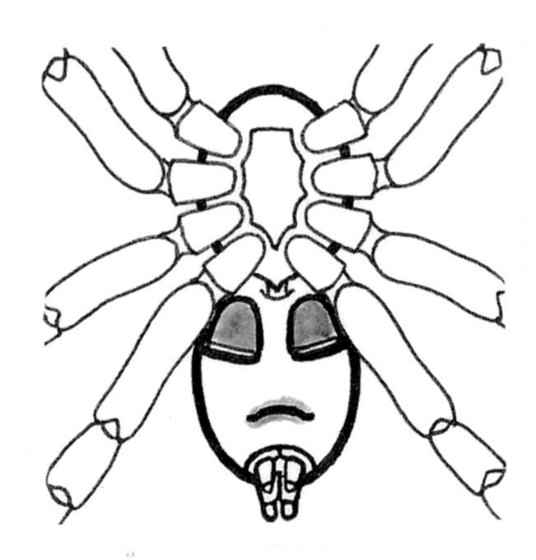

The book-lungs and trachea slit lie below the abdomen.

have four book-lungs; Araneomorphs (Modern spiders) have two, supplemented with a tracheal breathing system that may have one central opening (tracheal spiracle) or two. These lie behind the book-lungs on most Modern spiders.

EYES

Spiders do not have compound eyes, as insects do, but simple eyes (ocelli). Eye arrangement is often an identification guide. Most spiders have eight eyes set in two rows, although the curve of each row is so great

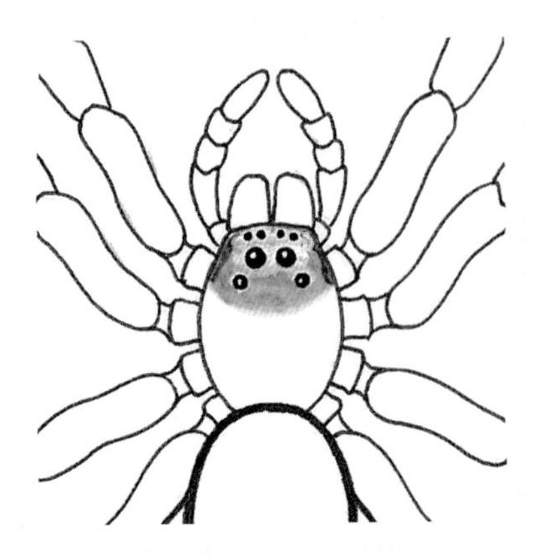

Most spider families have eight ocelli (eyes); some have six or less.

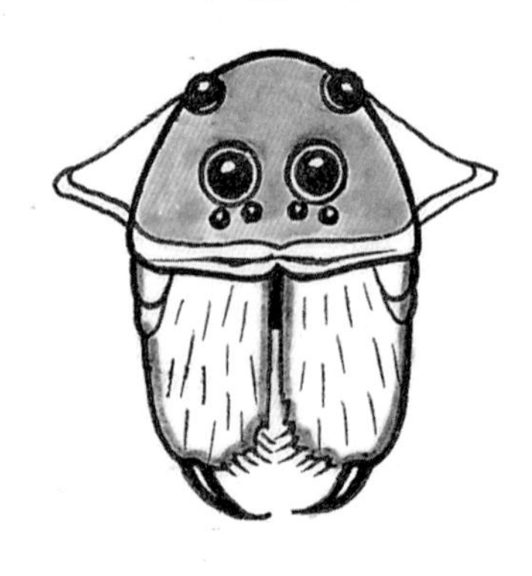

The caput (head region) bears the eyes.

A pair of five-jointed palps extends well ahead of the eyes.

Eyes, jaws and fangs of a Modern spider, *Typostola magnifica* (Heteropodidae).

in some species that the eyes are, in effect, arranged in three rows. Some species have 'lost' one or two pairs during evolution and have four or six eyes—e.g. Spitting spiders (family Scytodidae) and Feather-footed spiders (family Uloboridae).

FANGS AND JAWS

The jaws and fangs combine to form the chelicerae, the first pair of appendages of the cephalothorax, immediately ahead of the eyes. Each chelicera consists of two segments. The larger one, joined at the head to

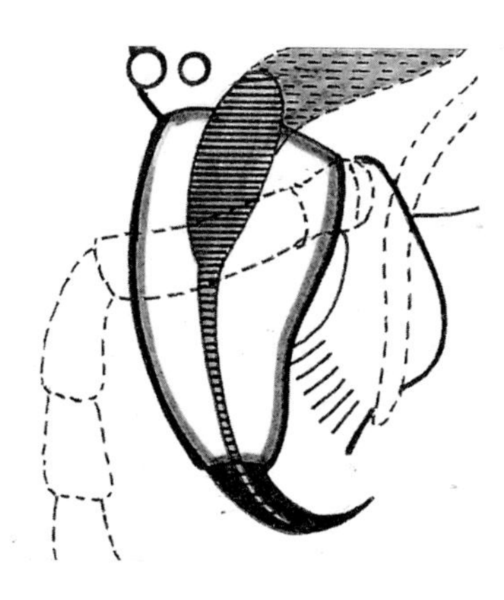

The poison glands lie in the fang bases of Primitives, and in the thorax in Moderns.

Eyes, jaws and fangs of a Primitive spider, *Atrax robustus* (Hexathelidae).

form the base segment, crushes prey and squeezes out its vital juices. The other is the fang segment, the needle-like apparatus that administers the venom. The chelicerae either point out horizontally from the body, as for all Primitive spiders (e.g. Funnel-webs and Trapdoors), or point vertically downward as they do in most Modern spiders (e.g. Wolf, Red-back and Wheel-weaving spiders).

MOUTH

The mouths of all spiders are similar in structure and function and well hidden behind the chelicerae. The mouth is bordered by an upper lip—the epistome or rostrum, and a lower lip—the labium. The labium is derived from a ventral segment or plate. A spider cannot eat solid food, so the vital juices of insect prey are squeezed out by the fang bases and maxillae (palpal base joints) and syphoned into the spider's mouth by powerful, sucking stomach muscles in the cephalothorax. The mouthparts filter the juices through tufts of stout hairs surrounding the 'jaws'.

Mouthparts, just ahead of sternum plate (Huntsman, *Delena cancerides*).

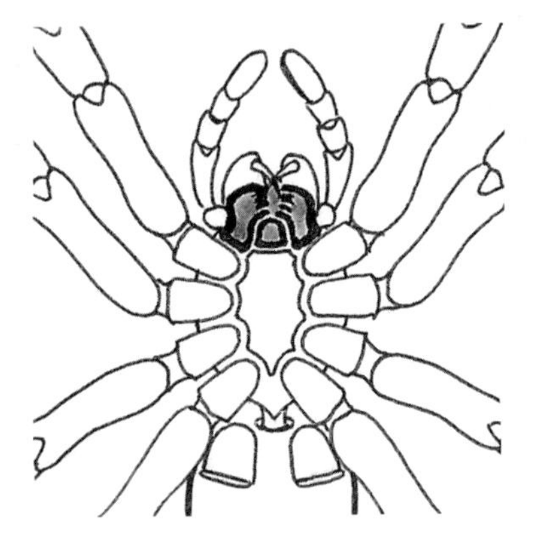

The mouthparts lie below the head, behind the fangs and fang bases.

PALPS

The palps of a male spider help to determine its species. These appendages project forward from the head region like the antennae of most insects and are commonly mistaken for legs. The palps are sensory organs and in both sexes they detect scents, sounds and vibrations. The male spider's palps are modified to act as sexual organs for storing and discharging sperm during mating.

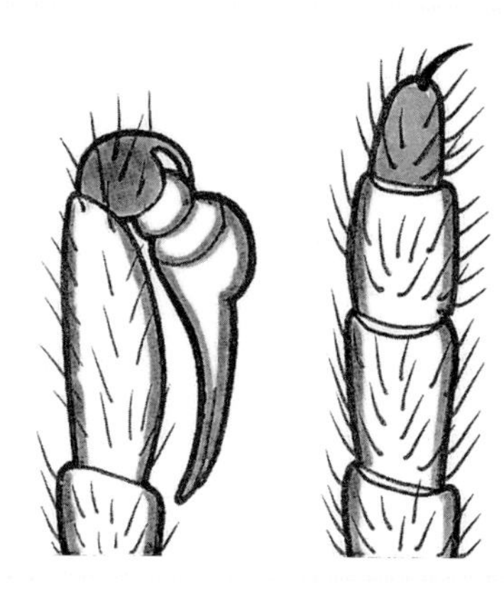
Male palps serve as sexual organs. Female palps serve as extendable mouthparts.

Palps of male Huntsman *Isopeda vasta* at final moult.

LEGS

A most important function for a spider is its ability to outmanoeuvre insect prey by means of eight nimble legs. These legs give it remarkable speed and the ability to negotiate rough terrain and silken threads. The legs also play an important role in web construction and in wrapping and handling entangled prey. Each leg consists of seven segments: starting from the ventral base of the body, these are the coxa, trochanter, femur, patella, tibia, metatarsus and the tarsus. Many species have on their

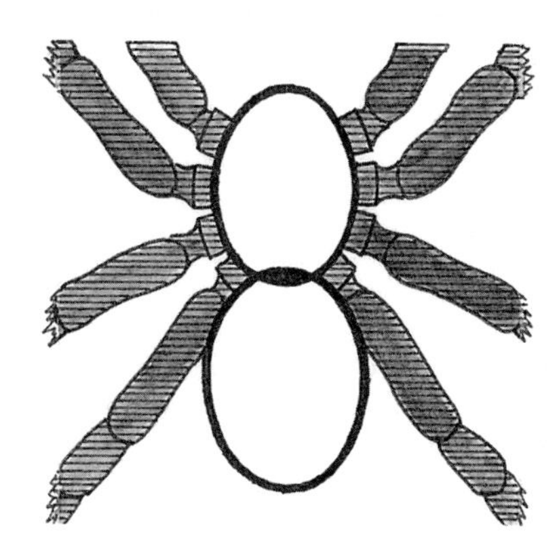
The eight legs are joined to the cephalothorax.

The legs have seven segments, ending in tarsal claws.

The legs surround the sternum plate; on most spiders two pairs point forward and two pairs point backward.

fourth tarsi special comb-shaped bristles for pulling out silk from the spinnerets.

The shape and length of the legs, their hairs, spines and spurs, and the number of claws on each tarsi are good identification guides for determining the family to which a particular individual belongs.

CLAWS

The tip of each leg as small but important structures: the claws, which can be likened to a cat's claw. Depending on the species, the spider's claws are modified to enable it to climb smooth vertical surfaces, run or skate over water, or grip a silken thread. According to the species, there may be two or three claws per tarsal tip and they may be supplemented with special brushes or tufts of hairs serving as suction pads, water buoys and climbing aids. The claws of a spider help us to identify its family but must be closely examined under a microscope.

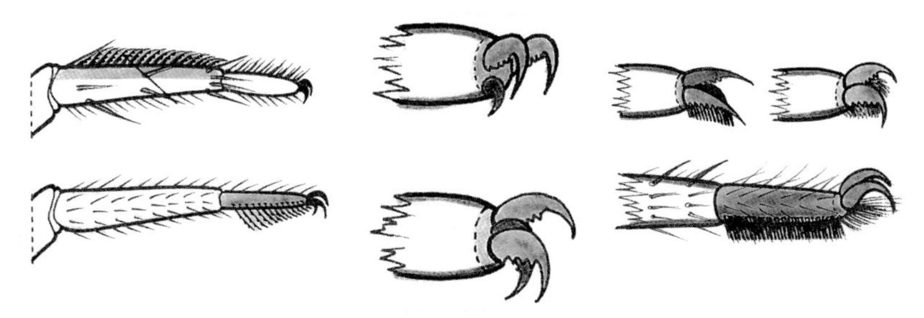

Spiders with a cribellum all have a calimistrum (rake or comb) on the hind legs.

The tips of the tarsi (feet) of most spiders bear three claws; some have two.

Two-clawed spiders usually have hair tufts for gripping slippery surfaces.

SPINNERETS

Beneath the abdomen towards the rear are amazing finger-like organs called spinnerets, through which the silk is extracted. Each spinneret may produce many different types of silk, which is supplied by various silk glands in the abdomen. The tip of each spinneret has numerous pores that operate like tiny taps, and each tap is connected to an individual tube leading to a special gland. The silk has to be drawn out by considerable

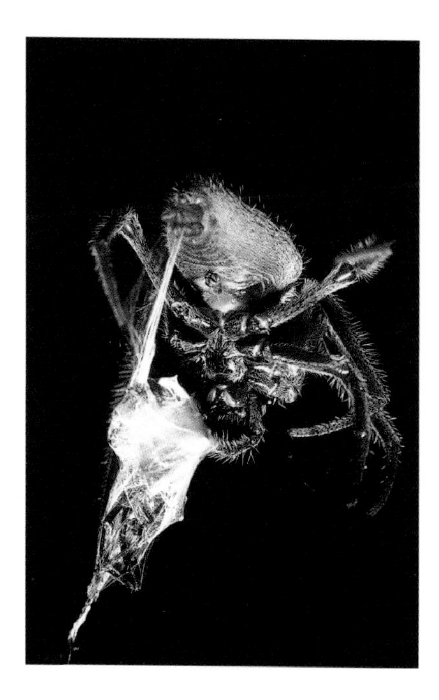

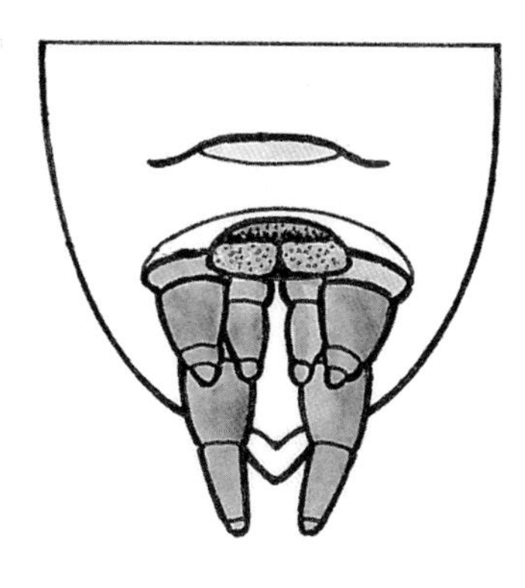

Many Modern spiders have a cribellum (spinning plate) ahead of the spinnerets.

Spinnerets of Wheel-weaving Garden spider *Eriophora transmarina*.

force, and the spider accomplishes this by using its hind tarsal combs, its body weight, or both. The number, size and shape of the spinnerets are useful guides for identifying a spider's family.

CRIBELLUM

Several Modern spiders have a narrow, oval plate ahead of the spinnerets. This 'spinning' plate is a modified organ, derived from a pair of spinnerets that have fused, and from this special organ broad bands of 'hackled' or woolly silk are combed out. Many web-weaving spiders produce this cribellate silk (e.g. Black House spiders of the genus *Badumna*). Species with a cribellum always have a complementary row of bristles on the metatarsus of the hindlegs, named the calimistrum. In some species this is hidden among hairs and difficult to see.

Cribellate silk.

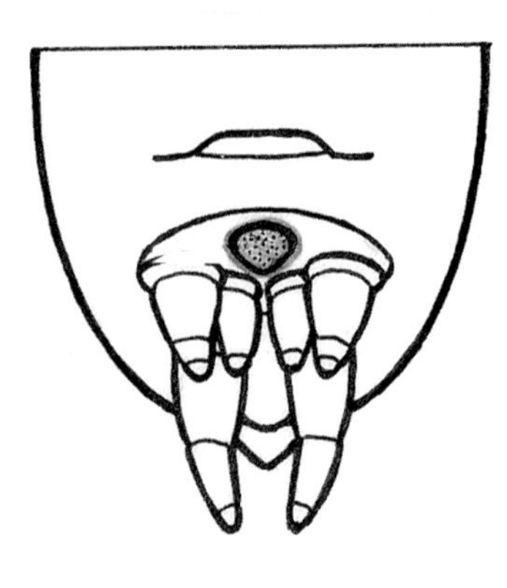

On some Moderns the cribellum is merely a bump, called the colulus.

SILK

Spider's silk is a complex albuminoid protein, secreted from special glands. Its composition is as follows: 25.3% alanine, 5.4% leucine, 42.8% glycine, 9.3% glutamine, 2.6% tyrosine, and traces of other amino acids—values calculated from a molecular clone of *Nemophila* silk. (This information was provided by Mr Theo Dopheide of Victoria).

Spiders produce an enormous range of silk textures, qualities and colours according to each species and its silk glands. Seven distinctly different types of silk glands are known, and each one manufactures a different silk for every need. No spider possesses all seven types but the genera *Eriophora* and *Argiope* (both Master Weavers) have five, and all spiders have at least three. The seven types are as follows.

- **Aciniform glands** feed silk through the median and posterior spinnerets. This type of silk is used for wrapping and packaging prey, as an outer covering for egg sacs, and for stabilamentum, as seen in the wheel webs of *Argiope*, family Araneidae.
- **Aggregate glands** feed viscid silk through the posterior spinnerets. This produces the prey-catching spiral threads used by the Master Weavers, family Araneidae.
- **Ampullate glands** feed dry silk through the anterior and median spinnerets for safety-lines, bridge lines, scaffolding and balloons for migration.
- **Cribellate glands** feed silk through the cribellum (spinning plate) and this type is highly elastic, blue-tinted and woolly. It is combed out by the calimistrum (bristles) on the hind legs.
- **Flageliform glands** feed silk through the posterior spinnerets and this type is used for making the sticky globules that hang from the whirling thread of Bolas spiders.
- **Pyriform glands** feed silk through the anterior spinnerets for attachment-discs to anchor bridge lines and web frames onto clay, bark, leaves and so on, and to bundle up prey.
- **Tubuliform glands** feed silk through the median and posterior spinnerets for constructing and insulating egg sacs, and lining shelters.

REPRODUCTION AND GROWTH

Spiderlings at second instar.

THE FEMALE REPRODUCTIVE SYSTEM: THE EPIGYNUM

Beneath the abdomen of the Modern female spider is a groove or furrow running cross-wise behind the book-lungs, and in the centre of this is the epigynum. It has an opening that leads to the internal reproduction organs, and also guides the tarsal palps of the male during mating. In many species this opening consists of two internal tubes: one receives the

Reproductive organs of a Modern female Wheel-weaving Garden spider *Eriophora transmarina*.

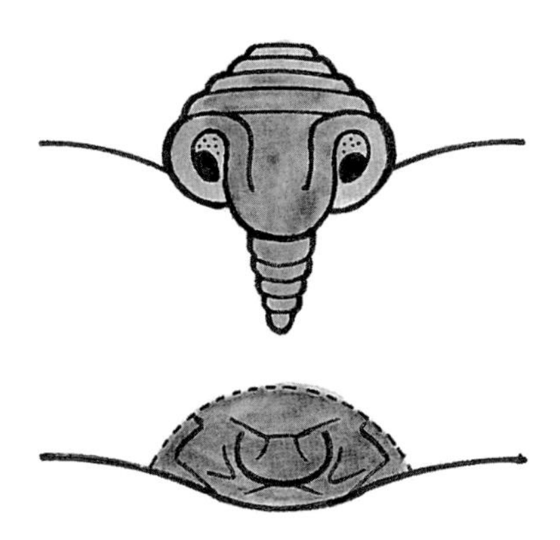

The epigynum's main function is to provide access to the internal genitalia.

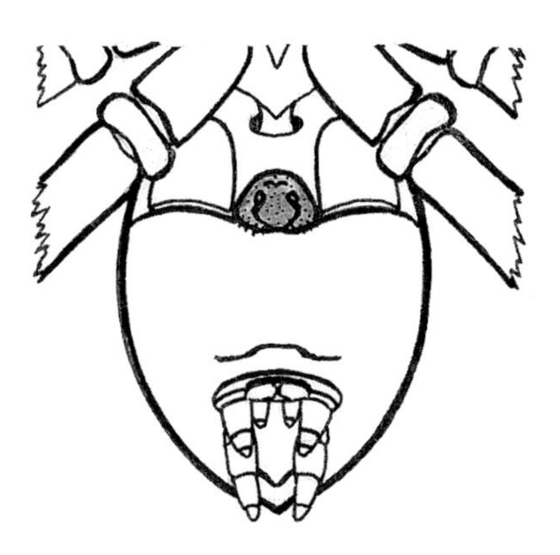

The epigynum (female genitalia) receives the male sperm, and leads to the ovaries.

Many Modern females have a pocket for storing the male's sperm.

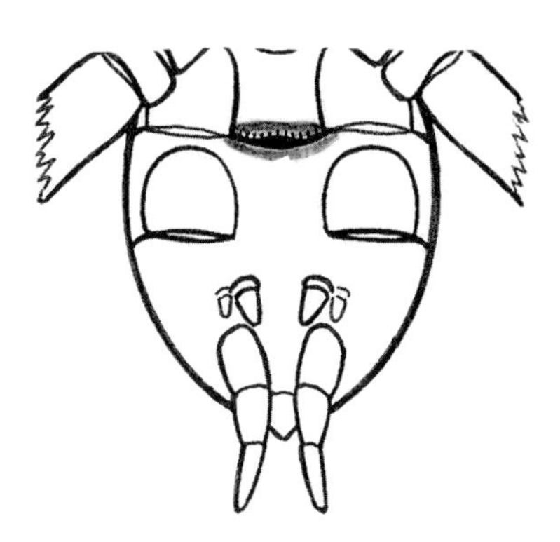

Primitive spiders have no epigynum.

sperm, and eggs produced by a pair of ovaries pass through the other. As the eggs pass down the female's egg-laying tube they are fertilised by the sperm released from her sperm pockets.

Most sexually mature female Araneomorphs (Modern spiders) have a visible sclerotised epigynum. Mygalomorphs (Primitive spiders) lack this external structure and some also lack the furrow or groove. Since the male Mygalomorph has many distinctive features characteristic of its species, scientists set pit-traps into the ground outside the female's burrow to collect males for identifying the species.

THE MALE REPRODUCTIVE SYSTEM: EMBOLI AND PALPAL BULBS

Unlike insects and most other animals, male spiders have no penis. Their reproductive organs, placed ventrally on the abdomen, consist of testes connected by a tube to a small opening. The male spins a small silken 'mat' onto which the sperm is discharged. It is then syphoned into the bulbous reservoirs of his palps. These palpal bulbs contain tubes called emboli. During a successful mating the sperm is discharged into the female's genital opening, where it may be stored or immediately used to fertilise the ovaries. Some Modern female spiders can store sperm for months.

Reproductive organs of a Primitive male—Red-headed Mouse, *Missulena insigne*.

The male sexual organ is guided by the epigynum during mating

COURTSHIP AND MATING

Very little is wasted in nature. The female spider's well-publicised practice of consuming her male counterpart is a fine example of nature's economy. Male spiders spend their whole life preparing for the time when they will mate. When they cast their final moult to become sexually mature, they cease feeding and dedicate all their energy to procreation. The female's agenda is different. Her greatest energy expenditure occurs after reproduction, when she must prepare for the onset of her brood. Her consumption of the male spider provides her with protein vital for this work.

The male's role is complete after mating. Exhausted, he will die anyway because he no longer has any interest in feeding himself. Of

Courtship and mating of Primitive spiders (Funnel-web, *Atrax robustus*).

Courtship and mating of Modern spiders (Huntsman, *Holconia* spp.).

Sexual dimorphism: the female aerial weaver (*Nephila*) dwarfs the male.

course, the male is not always eaten—depending on the species, he may successfully mate with several females. In certain species he may even cohabit with a female for a while before egg-laying, but is then chased out or eaten if he does not take the hint. But in every case he will not survive to mate the following season.

EGG PRODUCTION

Depending on the species, a spider may lay as many as 1,000 or more, or as few as five or less. An average spider (e.g. a Black House spider) lays about 100 eggs at one sitting. Most spiders construct a tough silken cocoon around the eggs to insulate them from climatic conditions and to deter insect predators, especially ants which carry them off to their nest to feed to their young. In some species the female spider stands guard

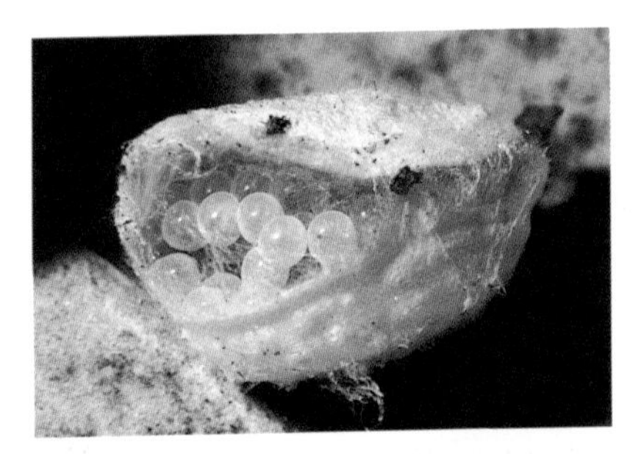

Top left Jumping spiders' eggs, well insulated in silken sacs.

Top right A Huntsman's egg sac.

Above Eggs are insulated to survive the coldest of winters.

Left After hours of spinning her egg sac, a female Huntsman rests at daybreak.

over her eggs, carries them about while hunting, encloses them in a curled leaf, seals them behind bark, or hides them in rock crevices.

EMBRYO AND INSTAR DEVELOPMENT

All spiders' eggs have a large yolk compared with that of most insects. This allows the embryo to develop to an advanced stage before the young emerge. All the essential characteristics of a spider are developed in the embryo stage. However, spiderlings differ from adults in that their mid-gut is a closed sac, isolated from the fore-gut and hind-gut, and filled with embryonic yolk. The embryonic spider starts to take shape on the outside of the egg yolk. Buds representing palps, legs and mouthparts sprout on the cephalothorax and a segmented abdomen appears at an early stage. However, except for four segments that develop into book-lungs and spinnerets, these abdominal segments disappear quickly.

There are two fundamental differences between the egg development of Primitive spiders and that of Modern spiders:

- Primitive spiders develop slowly, while Modern spiders develop quickly.
- In Primitive spiders the appendages grow outside the main egg-body and 'hang' off the yolk.

Young Wolf spiders clinging to their mother's knob-tipped hairs.

Time to disperse: spiderlings at second instar.

In Modern spiders all appendages are formed closely hugging the yolk to prevent moisture loss. These distinctions reflect the differences between the lifestyles of each group. For the Primitive spiders below ground, it is humid, cool and dark. This environment allows only slow development, but there is no risk of the embryo drying out. The above-ground Modern spiders, exposed to dryness, heat, light and a larger range of climatic conditions, develop faster but are prone to desiccation.

MOULTING

All baby spiders develop from the nourishment they derive from their egg yolk until they shed their second cuticle or exoskeleton. At this stage, a tendency to devour one another forces them to disperse. Most Modern spiders leave the nest-site by climbing to the top of a leaf, plant or rock, where each one plays out a flocculent balloon of silk. On this balloon the spiderling rises high into the air and is blown by the breeze to colonise new homesites, often far from the nest.

To continue growing, a spider has to shed its outgrown exoskeleton, whereupon rapid expansion occurs before the new cuticle hardens. Some species go through as many as ten moults before reaching sexual maturity. A spider nearly ready to moult appears to go through an uncomfortable process—several days before the event, it becomes inactive and loses all interest in feeding. During this rest period, the new exoskeleton layer forms beneath the old outgrown cuticle.

All spiders outgrow their exoskeletons; some moult as often as ten times.

Moulting is usually achieved during the cover of night and the spider may take up to an hour to free itself of its outmoded cuticle. Special glands release a 'moulting fluid' which greatly assists the process. Most Modern spiders hang from a silken thread as a means of protection from insect predators. In this position they squirm and wriggle about to make their old suit split up. The more heavily built Primitives lie on their backs in their burrow, legs uppermost as they shed the old cuticle. Casting off the large thoracic region is fairly straightforward and the soft abdominal cuticle usually shrivels off by itself. The most difficult stage of moulting is the slow removal of the legs from their restrictive outgrown armour. Imagine pulling your legs out of knee-length riding boots—but remember that the spider has four pairs of legs to extract!

The cicada, dragonfly and grasshopper (to name but a few examples) emerge from their nymphal skins by exactly the same process. The newly moulted spider is very soft and lacks pigmentation. For Modern spiders the new outer skeleton can take several hours to fully expand, harden and deepen in colour; for Primitive spiders it can take several days. Only after the final moult does the sex of the spider become distinct. However, many Modern sub-adult males develop bulbous palp tips before the final moult.

A spider casts off its skin just as this cicada does.

THE FOSSIL RECORD

Flattened Sac spider
Hemicloea.
Photo: Ross Perry.

The fossil record helps us to understand why animals and plants are as they are today. It has shown us that the spiders established themselves on land during the latter part of the Devonian Period, 360 million years ago, some 60 million years before the development of climbing and flying insects. During that period, spiders' prey chiefly consisted of ground-dwelling arthropods such as large silverfish, one-pronged bristletails, centipedes and wingless cockroach forms.

The fossil record shows that the climbing and flying insects made their appearance during the Carboniferous Period, 300 million years ago. The composition of the insect fauna of this period and its relationship with plants was very different from what it is today. More than 50% of the insect lifeforms displayed an astonishing variety of stylet-bearing and chewing or sucking mouthparts—less than 10% of today's insect fauna are equipped this way. For example, the primitive forms of butterflies had chewing mouthparts and ate the pollen of the earliest forms of flowering plants (angiosperms) which produced seeds enclosed in fruits.

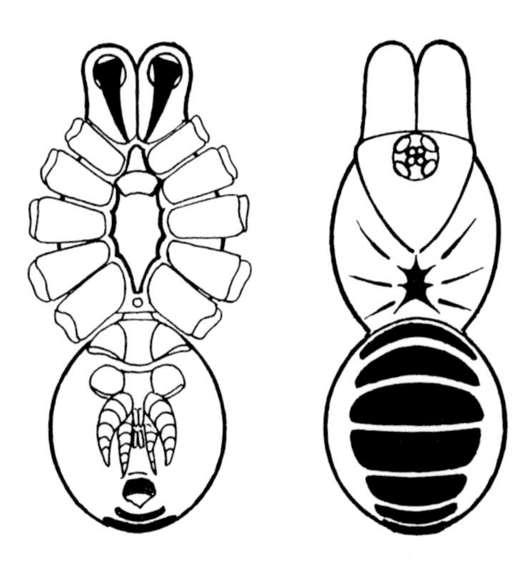

External anatomy of the earliest spider: Primitive segmented Trapdoor, suborder Liphistiomorphae (Mesothelae).

THE PLANTS LIFTED THE GAME

The climbing and flying insects, lured by succulent flowering plants, played a major part in the ascent of the spider fauna and their development of the use of silk for catching prey. It is because this development is so closely linked with the capture of prey that I have presented spiders in a sequence according to their method of hunting. There is a developmental progression from the Primitive home-bound Funnel-web and Trapdoor spiders, which sit in dark holes waiting to grab at stumbling prey, to that of the Modern aerial, acrobatic Wheel-weaving spiders, which have developed silk constructions to ensare flying insects.

In between these extremes of capture techniques are the Open-range Hunters, the Ambushers and Anglers and the Apprentice Weavers. Not until the latter group made their appearance over 100 million years ago during the Cretaceous Period were the first true silken webs developed for the efficient capture of insects. These were three-dimensional, often messy-looking webs, strung from plants and structures off the ground. Then came the Master Weavers with their two-dimensional wheel-webs, and their approach to web-making is a manifestation of their efficiency and economy of silk, time and energy, and represents the pinnacle of the spiders' snare-making skills.

Euro permunda well preserved in amber—a rare relic of the Oligocene Epoch, 38 million years old.

THE DEVELOPMENT OF SPIDERS

A Modern spider,
Tetragnatha rubiventris.

PRIMITIVE SPIDERS: MYGALOMORPHS

The ancestral lineage of Mygalomorphs goes back over 360 million years. Most of these spiders still live fearful lives in damp, dark holes in the ground and react to unexpected events by cowering in fear, unable to move, or by violently plunging their pick-axe fangs into whatever is in striking range. They take several years to reach maturity. The females, in particular, are known to live long, sedentary lives of 20 years or more. The males rarely survive the fifth year after shedding their final moult. Once the urge to procreate is gone, they lose all interest in feeding (as all male spiders do). Some of the largest, most aggressive and most poisonous spiders belong to this suborder.

There are three major groups of Primitive spiders in Australia: the Trapdoors, Funnel-webs and Brush-footed Trapdoors. They are all survivors from times when much of the land was covered in great forests and have not really changed much from their ancestral forms. Although the males venture out during the mating season, the females rarely move far from their dark abode and restrict themselves to feeding on unwary ground-dwelling insects that pass near the burrow entrance at night.

Female Funnel-webs never leave their retreat unless forced to by flooding or some other disturbance. Trapdoor spiders leave their burrow only to catch prey that passes by. Some of the more recently evolved Mygalomorphs, such as the Brushfooted Trapdoors, do leave their burrow at night to hunt for prey and often attack climbing and winged diurnal insects resting among the foliage, tree trunks and rocks.

MODERN SPIDERS: ARANEOMORPHS

Araneomorphs are the most common form of present-day spider. Exactly when these spiders branched from the basic stock of their four-gilled ancestors remains controversial. Dramatically changing climates, the marked stages of insect metamorphosis including the power of flight and dispersal, and the diminishing of rich green forests all contributed to their break away from the archetypal or common stock. The development of drier, more open vegetation during the Cretaceous Period over 100 million years ago led to many spiders adopting diverse survival skills and body structure.

Araneomorphs are extremely diversified in physical make-up as well as in habits and environmental preferences, but can be separated into two broad categories: Vagrant-wandering spiders, and Web-weaving spiders. To present them in clearer terms, they are separated here into four categories according to prey-capturing techniques and uses of silk: Open-range Hunters; Ambushers and Anglers; Apprentice Weavers; Master Weavers.

There are no primitive animals living now, as every animal (including all arachnids) is in fact composed of a mass of specialisations and the form or body structure alone is a vestige of the primitive condition. All growth is the result of life's experimentation, the process of trial and error. However, the hypothesis of an evolution taking place only by slow degrees is not always in accordance with the facts.

OPEN-RANGE HUNTERS

Australia's Open Range Hunters Group consists of 28 families and 853 species and represents 45% of Australia's described spiders. The best way to represent this group is to present the dominant families, those we're most familiar with—for example, Wolf and Huntsman spiders.

AMBUSHERS AND ANGLERS

The Ambushers and Anglers Group consists of seven families and 200 species. It represents about 10% of Australia's described spiders. The members do not necessarily have a common origin. At some stage in their long evolution they have all made changes in their habits of either living in rock crevices below ground or relying on silken snares to capture prey. They have become Ambushers and Anglers and strategically position themselves amongst the haunts of insects, remaining still and patient, their colouring merging with their surroundings. As soon as an insect moves within capture range, the spider either pounces upon it, reels it in on a line or drops a silken net over it.

APPRENTICE WEAVERS

This group consists of 20 families and 270 species. It represents about 14% of Australia's described spiders, including those that pioneered silk-weaving to make snares anchored to plants and rocks, often well above the ground. These snares are three-dimensional and come in many designs. They not only catch prey but also give some protection from predators. Unlike the Mygalomorphs and most of the Open-range Hunters, these spiders do not overreact to every movement. Instead, they investigate situations to avoid contact with dangerous prey, and weave their ingenious snares amidst the favourite haunts of climbing and flying insects. All members are three-clawed without tufts and generally have eight eyes set in two rows of four. The earliest forms of snare construction made by Apprentice Weavers are associated with the modification of their first pair of spinnerets that have become fused to form a spinning plate—the cribellum.

MASTER WEAVERS

This group consists of six families, 36 genera and 340 species. It represents about 17% of Australia's described spiders and 90% of the Master Weavers belong to the family Araneidae. Most of us, at one time or another, have beheld a dew-covered wheel of silk hanging from the bushes and glistening in the morning sun. All these spiders build wheel-webs and their method of prey capture is far and away the most successful in terms of energy efficiency alone. Built between the flight paths of insects, these two-dimensional snares, with their symmetrical 'wheel', economise on a spider's silk, time and energy and demonstrate the spider's keen observations of insect behaviour.

Having eliminated the need to hunt for prey, the Master Weavers rely entirely upon silk for every aspect of their life. The wheel-web, built with mathematical precision, represents the pinnacle of spider silk evolution. By comparison with all other snares, the wheel-web has distinct advantages. It spans generous areas with the minimum of silk. Its design allows the spider to move along the geometric pattern of radii while making minimal contact with the sticky spiral. When any portion of the web is touched, the vibrations are immediately relayed to the hub, where the spider waits patiently for its food to arrive.

WHERE TO FIND SPIDERS

A juvenile Red-back, *Latrodectus hasselti*.

The best places to find most Mygalomorphs (Primitive spiders) and the ground-dwelling Open Range Araneomorphs (Modern spiders) are habitats that provide plenty of shelter and are close to a river, stream or creek where abundant plantlife attracts insects. These spiders make their retreats in any form of ground cover such as fallen timber, leaf litter, cracks and crevices in rocks and soil, exposed tree roots and so on.

When searching for Apprentice Weavers and Master Weavers such as Platform, Lace-web and Golden Orb-weaving spiders, look for sites that provide anchor points for snare constructions amongst foliage, timber and rocks and places where there are climbing and flying insects. Tree trunks and foliage provide favourite hunting sites for many of the Open-range Hunters (e.g. Huntsman), and the Ambushers and Anglers (e.g. Sac and Crab spiders).

Rock ledges, bark, fallen timber and hollow tree stumps are all favourite retreats, especially near streams and creeks where insects flourish. Climbing and flying insects such as grasshoppers, locusts, stoneflies, dragonflies, damselflies, cicadas, flies, beetles, bees, butterflies and moths form the staple diet of most Araneomorphs (Modern spiders). Crawling, ground-dwelling insects such as earwigs, native cockroaches, crickets, beetles, silverfish, springtails, numerous insect larvae and earthworms form the staple diet of the Mygalomorphs (Primitive spiders).

Dusk to dawn is an ideal time to observe most species, as this is when they are most active in hunting, building snares, performing courtship rituals, mating, egg-laying and so on. Go spider-watching well prepared—take a 35 mm single-reflex camera with close-up lens or extension tubes for magnification, and a small flashlight. A video recorder is ideal for photographing events as they occur. A

Look for spiders among foliage, timber and rocks that provide cover and anchor points for their snares.

field notebook, record sheet, and a cassette player for recording your observations (along with forest sounds) are good basic tools, especially if you wish to share your well-earned observations and experiences with others. A few unbreakable containers are also necessary for transporting interesting spiders for your observation cage. Note that a permit is required for collecting in National Parks.

Once you have found a spider that interests you, several things must be thought about, as there is still so little known about even the most common spiders. Make a note of all relevant data such as the time of the day, date, weather conditions, type of habitat, and associations with other lifeforms in the spider's immediate surroundings. Try to determine its genus or family. This way you can compile a valuable and orderly record of your finds, their environmental requirements, and the impact they have on a particular ecosystem.

Try to estimate the population of the species itself and that of other spiders occupying its immediate surroundings. Record in your notebook whether it was (a) common; (b) moderately common; (c) rare. Also note its niche preferences, the nature of the area and the consistency of the type of habitat. Allow for any changes to the ecosystem such as recent bushfires, floods, use of sprays and the removal of any vegetation in land-clearing.

The status (abundancy) of any particular species varies at different times of the year, as most species have definite breeding periods. In tropical regions there are normally large numbers of species dispersed in their respective niches close to one another because of the enormous range of available micro-habitats. In temperate regions species are fewer, with far less overlapping of niches. Look for general patterns in the number of species co-existing in certain habitats and try to find evidence to explain these patterns. Competition between species, availability of retreat-shelter or snare-construction sites, availability of insect prey and the temperature and elevation are all influencing factors.

HOW TO LOOK AFTER SPIDERS IN CAPTIVITY

To learn the more intimate aspects of spider behaviour and to determine unfamiliar species, you may wish to place your specimens in simulated conditions inside an aquarium or the like at home for a while, after which you can return them to their natural habitat. Any fine mesh cage or glass/plastic container at least 20 cm across, round or square, will do. Of course, a glass aquarium maximises viewing.

Never crowd spiders, as they are cannibalistic and will attack one another, the larger overpowering the smaller. Some of the diurnal

A sliding panel allows the male and female to meet during the breeding season. Photo: Eugene Hodgens, designer of this observation house.

Large sturdy glass jars are ideal for observing a female's maternal phases.

(daylight) hunters such as the Jumping, Crab, Flower and Triangular spiders tolerate one another fairly well so long as insect prey is available. However, aggressive open-range hunters such as Wolf, Huntsman, Sac and Nursery-web spiders readily attack one another in captivity, insects provided or not. Some of the snare-makers such as Redback, Platform and Black House spiders usually make themselves at home without complaint or aggression.

Silken tube retreat of a female Funnel-web, *Atrax robustus*, in a glass spider-house. Photo: Eugene Hodgens.

The larger wheel-weavers such as the Garden spiders (*Eriophora*) and Golden-Orb-weaving spiders (*Nephila*) become very confused in confined quarters, as they require ample space to spread their marvellous wheel-web snares. Very few, if any, female Primitive spiders tolerate one another's company in confined spaces, as their territorial (ownership) instinct demands a certain 'comfort zone' to live in. The most successful method of keeping Funnel-web, Trapdoor and Brush-footed Trapdoor spiders alive and healthy is to place only one spider per observation cage.

A male and female of the same species may find each other acceptable for a time during the breeding season, but there is no guarantee of this. A female mother spider tending her young is an exception and these should be kept together, free from interference from other spiders. These are some of the things you will soon find out for yourself. The container needs a lid design that will allow you to place live insects into the cage without letting them or the spider escape. Many spiders (e.g. Brushfooted Trapdoor, Huntsman, Sac and Jumping spiders) are equipped with special 'suction-pad feet' (special oiled brushes), and can run up smooth vertical surfaces with ease.

You need to be quick when placing insect prey into the cage to feed the spider. A close-fitting lid with a small spring door is ideal. However, a stout sheet of class (weighted with a book etc.) works well because you can slide it open just as far as you need. An elasticised netting such as stocking material can serve as a lid in some situations, especially on the tops of round containers. *Always keep the spiders well out of the reach of small children and pets.*

The viewing box of your miniature theatre needs a layer of river sand or soil. Burrowers such as Wolf and Trapdoor spiders need enough sand or soil to be able to dig a shallow burrow in which to retire. 60 mm of sand, soil or fine gravel is ample. You also need to add a couple of small flat rocks, a piece of bark, a few dry leaves and some twigs to give the spider surroundings that are as natural as possible. Do not add so much that you make it hard to view the spider.

Note: Never use potting mixes or composted garden soil, as bacteria and fungi rapidly build up and can kill the occupant/s. Never drop in insects that have been sprayed with any form of insecticide, nor offer predatory insects such as mantids, tree crickets, assassin bugs, wasps, or any stinging, biting insects that could injure or kill the spider/s. Offer only prey that the spider would normally capture in its natural habitat, such as cockroaches, moths, flies, beetles and insect larvae. Dead insects are useless to spiders, as they feed only on freshly killed or moving prey, refusing all else. Also, rotting or dead matter causes disease and creates an unhealthy environment.

Unhealthy spiders are not very active, nor do they have good appetites, so there will be little to watch or learn about them. The observation cage must be kept clean and this is easily maintained by not letting dead matter accumulate and by not over-watering. Spiders need to drink, but do not like the sand or soil saturated. Even though they enjoy humid, cool conditions, they do not like being soaked, let alone waterlogged. A wad of cotton-wool laid on a piece of foil in one corner of the cage and sprinkled with water allows the spider to drink as required and will also maintain enough humidity. Keep your observation tank on a shelf or on the floor in a cool, semi-dark corner if possible. At times an atomiser is useful, especially in hot, dry weather, as a fine mist will not cause the overwatering problems that sprinkling can.

When you are satisfied that you have studied some particular phase of the lifecycle of a particular spider, release it—preferably where you found it. This may be several weeks later, depending on the observation period you need. Always try to return the spider where it has the best chances of survival. Do not introduce species into areas where they would not normally occur, as this can create problems for the local spider fauna. For more about this see the habitat information accompanying each species listed.

So far as collecting spiders for pickling is concerned, pickled spiders are useful if not necessary for reference work involved in identification, but disclose little about their life history. Use the reference collections at museums for identification.

Specimens are best preserved in 80% ethyl alcohol, with a little glycerine to stop them becoming brittle. They can be supported on glass and held in position with nylon fishing line. Photo: Eugene Hodgens.

A successful method for capturing male Funnel-web and Trapdoor spiders for observation is to sink pit-traps into the ground alongside the entrance to the female burrow. Your pit-traps, preferably large glass jars 18 cm deep, must be smooth. Funnel-web and Trapdoor spiders (except the Brushfooted species) cannot climb smooth, vertical surfaces and will remain huddled together.

A smooth vertical surface also deters marauding ants. Sink the trap into the ground up to its rim just outside the burrow entrance. Add a little sand to the jar to help cushion the fall as the male spiders tumble in during the night. Mature male spiders do not normally attack one another, as they focus entirely on finding a female spider to mate with. The feeding instinct is entirely replaced with the urge to reproduce their kind.

The breeding habits of secretive animals are especially hard to study; for example, Trapdoor and Funnel-web spiders lay their eggs inside their burrow, enclosed in a silken cocoon and fixed to the wall or main shaft. The spiderlings remain with the mother until they are about 8 months old, at which time they disperse to set up their own home nearby. To learn the ways of spiders you need to be patient and vigilant. The thrill of uncovering some of the secrets of these remarkably ancient creatures is reward enough to spur on the naturalist.

DRAWING, PHOTOGRAPHING AND MAKING NOTES

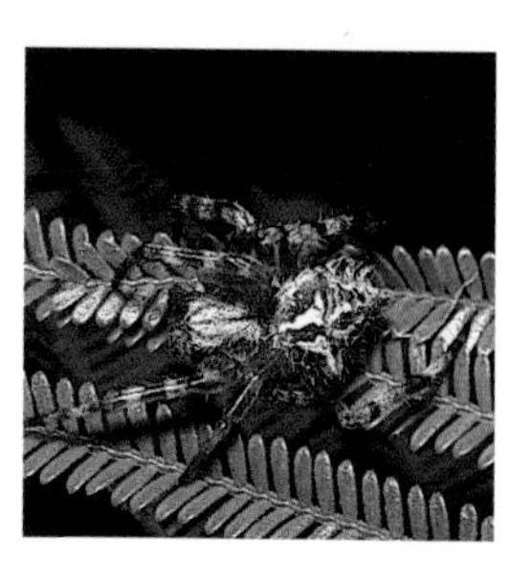

A Wheel-weaver, *Eriophora heroine*.

DRAWING

One drawing well done can be clearer than hundreds of words of description. The very act of drawing forces you to focus, observe and record details and important information. It is surprising how often you may describe a spider in words and then find that your general impressions do not stand the test of an accurate drawing. A line drawing in black and white is a severe exercise in economy of means, and forces you to decide firmly whether or not a detail is present.

As a discipline alone, drawing is well worth practising. Shading and effects of roundness can be indicated rather than portrayed and the simplest methods are usually the most successful. To shade a bigger area, two standard methods are used with great success: stippling and cross-hatching (line-shading). Stippling involves filling in an area with dots of varied size and spacing. The basic requirements, apart from practice, are patience and deliberation. You can erase unwanted lines and dots etc. by spotting them out with white liquid paper. When you draw a spider or insect you will often be copying from a cabinet-mounted specimen (wet or dried) and if the arrangement of its limbs or appendages looks unnatural, you can adjust this.

RELAXING SPECIMENS

Do not attempt to move the limbs of a dried specimen until it is relaxed. Relaxing fluid can be made up with water (about 25 ml) and a quarter of a teaspoon of chlorocresol to prevent the development of mould. Put some absorbent material such as cotton-wool or a dishwashing sponge into the base of an airtight container and pour the relaxing fluid over it until it is saturated. Then add a sheet of foam, as specimens should not be in contact with the fluid. It can take from one to five days to soften the specimen. Test by gently touching one of its limbs: if it doesn't move, relax it further for another day or two. When fully relaxed, the body and limbs can be spread into a more natural position.

Pin the specimen on cork, foam or soft wood. Allow a generous margin around it for safe handling, for you may need to manoeuvre the setting board to examine closely a particular feature. A simple line drawing is what you are aiming for. Depending on how much representation of form you wish to give it, various methods of pen strokes can be used in the final stages.

TOOLKIT

This should include a non-smudging rubber, sharp pencils (2B and HB), a ruler, assorted nibbed pens (hollow-nib pens are ideal for this work), indian ink, and a magnifying glass—x 3 magnification will give a complete coverage of the subject. You also need a microscope for tiny specimens. If the spider or insect is not too small, you can copy it quite easily without magnifying it. First make a preliminary sketch, as your first aim is to supply line information only.

SHAPE OUTLINE

The spider viewed from directly above can be portrayed as symmetrical in the finished drawing, as this makes the process easier. When you have drawn one half of the subject (left or right) and are satisfied that it's reasonably accurate, trace it onto a fresh piece of paper with a 2B pencil. Then turn the tracing upside down and align it with the half drawing you've done. Rub the paper firmly with a finger nail or the end of a paint brush to transfer the image.

You should now have a general shape that looks okay. When you are happy about the pencilled image, go over it with a mapping pen or rapidograph. Make sure your drawing is of a size and shape that will reduce to fit onto a page without wasting space. An enormous drawing full of fine details will not reduce well and a tiny thumbnail sketch will not enlarge well. A drawing reproduces best if it is four times larger than the subject.

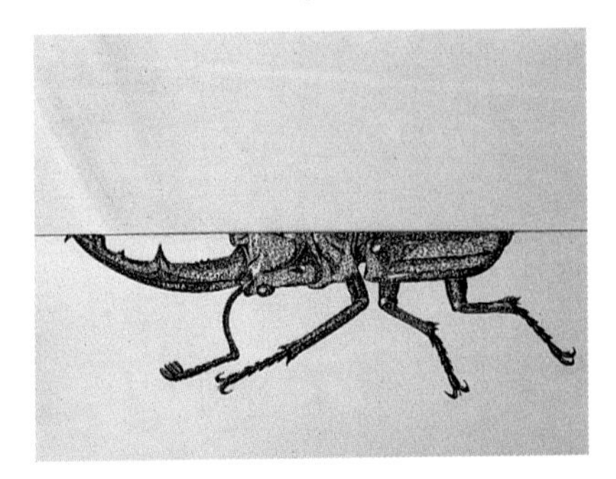

Draw one half of the subject, then trace this image to complete it.

USING A SCALE

To show people the actual size of the spider or insect you have drawn, you need to supply a measurement. For example, suppose you have completed a drawing or a painting of a butterfly. The specimen you copied measures

100 mm with its wings outspread, yet your drawing may measure 300 mm. Choose a number between 1 to 9 (e.g. 4) and divide the 300 mm by 4: this gives you 75 mm. Now divide 100 mm (actual size) also by 4: this gives you a scale of 25 mm. Now simply draw a line measuring 75 mm beneath your drawing and write on it '25 mm', as this is what your 75 mm line represents.

PHOTOGRAPHING SPIDERS

Buy the best equipment that you can afford. This applies especially to lenses, because the images you capture on film are only as good as the optics that created them. There are three important aspects to bear in mind: (1) technical quality; (2) scientific value; (3) artistic quality.

TECHNICAL QUALITY

Focusing. Use the best lens for the job, and make certain that you have the head and eyes of the subject in distinct, sharp focus. The rest of its body will be acceptable in softer focus and can actually help to highlight the features you wish to emphasise.

Framing. Include as much of the spider and its immediate surroundings as practically possible for its size. Careful cropping is essential for highlighting a particular aspect of the subject that you intend the viewer to focus upon.

Lighting. It is important to achieve really clear results and a flashlight ensures this. For the best lighting, try to combine sunlight with flashlight, using the flashlight for various effects—for eliminating or accentuating shadows, for example. The flashlight should complement the natural light but not override it. Photographing the subject against a light-coloured background helps you make a good exposure, vice versa if the subject is lightly toned.

Film grain. A fine grain film is best for this type of close-up work. ASA 64 Kodachrome, Ectachrome or Fujichrome are ideal and will stand up to enlarging without problems. The resolution of transparency film can be as high as 20 million pixels per 35 mm.

SCIENTIFIC VALUE

This is achieved only if you show the outstanding features of the spider, its homesite, its nestsite, its young, and the special features of its natural habitat. Also include any other creature associated with the spider.

Identifying features. Always attempt to present an image of the spider that will show a characteristic feature of the species. If this is not evident in the photograph, it simply doesn't exist for the viewer, who is unable to examine the flat plane of the two-dimensional film.

Homesites and nestsites. A spider's homesite or nestsite often discloses valuable information about the life-history of a particular species and its relationship with other lifeforms. The maternal instincts of certain species such as Wolf spiders are tremendously strong.

The young. Photographs showing different stages of a particular spider are especially interesting because although the adults of several species are well known, their young are not. When adults and immature spiders are found together, the opportunity of a valuable record should not be missed.

Habitat features. These tell their own story and give the viewer a considerable amount of information such as plant relationships, and soil and water relationships. This is an important aspect of photographing spiders. When photographing those that rely on cryptic camouflage for their survival, use frontal lighting only. Side lighting produces an obvious body shadow along one side. This could well ruin an otherwise convincing camouflage photograph.

Note: Whereas a photograph of a dead spider or insect usually gives only a poor reminder of what it looked like when it was alive, a colour photograph of the living creature in its natural habitat may well disclose much more information than can be seen with the naked eye.

ARTISTIC QUALITY

This involves contrasts of colour, composition, selection of statement or viewpoint, and capturing the behaviour of spiders in their natural habitat.

Colour contrasts. Select a viewpoint so that the subject is well defined in the photograph; the subject and its background will determine whether frontal, back or side lighting should be used. If you need to define the subject by using coloured background cards, they must be carefully chosen. Blues, greens and browns are highly suitable. A colour card can be very useful if the spider is surrounded by so much clutter and debris that it becomes lost—the card will help to define it in the finished photograph.

Composition. Avoid the habit of positioning the subject always in the centre of the frame. Try to include some of the surrounding habitat. Keep a small pair of scissors or snips in your kit so that you can remove any obstructive leaf, stem or grassblade out of the way of the camera lens.

Statement or viewpoint. This is where we come to personal choice—what we want to show the viewer. Photographs of spiders vary enormously according to the viewpoint we select. Photographing them at their own level helps bring the viewer into the realm of the spider; photographing them from above diminishes them. Photographing from the side or profile gives a detached effect, while taking the subject from below adds a dramatic touch and can make the subject look formidable indeed. So when taking a photograph of a particular spider, consider carefully what you intend to communicate.

Behaviour of subject. Knowing your subject is a distinct advantage when photographing spiders and insects. Animals have a discomfort zone and if you remain outside it they will carry on with their activities. Enter their 'fear circle' and they will move away. However, this behaviour can be used to create wonderful photographs. For example, a beetle usually opens its wings in preparation for flight the moment it crawls to the tip of a twig held at an angle leading upwards. If a butterfly is photographed feeding with its wings half opened, you can show both aspects—the dorsal (upper) and ventral (lower) aspects of its wing patterns and colours as it moves from flower to flower. Series of photographs of spiders showing behaviour during feeding, courtship, mating and so on, are potentially full of interest. Dragonflies, butterflies and cicadas offer opportunities galore for exciting photograph sequences as they emerge from their nymphal skins and pupae.

Equipment. In the field, the aim is to photograph the spider or insect in its ecological context, rather than fill up the frame with it (unless specific features are to be shown close-up). Hand-holding the camera is most practical when quick changes of framing the subject must be made in a hurry. The motion-stopping short duration of the flashlight is one of the most helpful pieces of equipment for the close-up nature photographer. It also allows you to use smaller apertures to provide the

Some basic equipment for close-up photography: 35 mm SLR camera with manual exposure control; compact handheld flash-light with extension cord; 55 mm lens and lens hood; small tripod; interchange-able extension tubes for magnification.

additional depth of field (range of sharp focus) so greatly needed in close-up work.

Extension tubes can be used in conjunction with the standard lens. A macro lens with a two-element diopter combined with flash is also a good combination. If you don't want to scare off the highly mobile creature in front of you, fitting a diopter onto the end of the lens for greater magnification is easier than screwing an extension tube between the lens and camera body. A skylight filter should at all times be fitted to the front of your camera to protect the lens and to reduce flareback to the minimum. Sometimes a polarising filter is useful, especially when photographing glossy spiders such as Funnel-webs, or insects in water habitats where water reflections cause flareback. A tripod is useful for setting up your camera to photograph a single flower head over several hours.

MAKING NOTES

You will not get far in studying spiders before uncovering some interesting aspects of their life history which have not been written about, aspects no-one else seems to have noticed and recorded before. If you study almost any group of spiders, you will be astonished to find how little is really known about them with certainty. However modestly you start out as a beginner, anxious to learn from the experts, sooner or later you will gain some information that you feel compelled to pass on to others. The first essential step when writing observation notes is to confine them to your immediate subject and not be baffled or confused by the immensity of the field of study. Choose one family, one genus, one small group of arthropods and study them thoroughly and precisely.

Be tidy. Collect your observations in an orderly way, file them properly (a 5x3 card system is fine). Whenever you make notes on odd scraps of paper or in old exercise books, transfer them onto cards as soon as possible. Because cards can be filed in an orderly arrangement, they can be assembled with a definite purpose, and this way a paper such as a review of a small group of arthropods or a monograph of a family can be built up quite easily. All work for publication is made much easier by this system.

Don't play with names. Writing about names isn't your first concern in Araneology (the study of spiders). When you begin to study the arachnids don't become side-tracked into playing with their names. As Winston Churchill remarked, 'We must beware of needless innovations, especially when guided by logic alone'.

MYGALOMORPHAE
Primitive spiders

A Trapdoor waiting for prey.

The Mygalomorph suborder consists of 10 families and 241 species and represents 13% of Australia's described spiders.

All Primitive spiders rely on the cover of darkness to catch prey with their huge pick-axe fangs. All have nocturnal mating and feeding habits and, compared with many Modern spiders, have poor eyesight. They live fearful lives, some ready to attack at the slightest disturbance, while others become immobile, feigning death. The female Primitive spider guards her egg sac by either resting with her front feet on it or sitting on it as a hen broods on her eggs. When prey is very scarce, adults have been known to fast for almost two years.

Not one species of Primitive spider has evolved a silken snare specifically to entangle insect prey and hold it fast. Most prey is captured whenever it happens to venture near a spider's hole or burrow. Even though some species set down trip-lines that radiate from the burrow entrance to relay the presence of prey, this seems to be as much as they have achieved with silk, mostly because of their sedentary, very long lives (20 years or more). By contrast, the highly active Modern Araneomorphs rarely live for more than two years, and their vastly greater generation turnover has led to their greater adaptability in keeping abreast of the flying insects.

Spiders that live below the ground are usually well protected from bushfires and floods. The thick insulation of soil above the burrow means that a fire may pass overhead without injury to the occupants below. During prolonged floods, Trapdoor, Funnel-web and Brushfooted Trapdoor spiders are generally safe—Primitive spiders are well versed in surviving such conditions. Several Trapdoor spiders cement their lids shut and Funnel-webs spin a stout curtain of silk across the entrance. The Brushfooted Trapdoors spin themselves silken socks and seal themselves inside them. They retire to special side chambers running off the main shaft of the tunnel, and their hair-covered bodies trap sufficient oxygen to sustain them for long periods.

The distinctive external features of Primitive spiders are as follows.

- **Chelicerae:** fang base and fang tip segments, aligned horizontally with the body and sitting parallel to one another.
- **Fang tips:** hinged in such a way that they move in pick-axe fashion (paraxial movement) when stabbing prey; they do not meet at the tips.

- **Palps:** leg-like appendages between the chelicerae and the first pair of legs, and usually long, particularly in the males.
- **Two pairs of book-lungs:** gill-like respiratory breathing system.
- **Four spinnerets:** occasionally six; the anterior median spinnerets on Modern spiders are never present.
- **Cribellum or colulus:** never present on Primitive spiders.
- **Paired sigilla:** external depressions representing the points of muscle and tendon attachment, on the sternum plate.
- **Haplogyne vulva:** vulva that have the same ducts for both insemination and fertilisation.
- **Abdomen:** entirely without segments except for the suborder Liphistiomorphae (not found in Australia).

BURROW ENTRANCE

TRAPDOOR

Australia's five Trapdoor families—Ctenizidae, Idiopidae, Actinopodidae, Migidae and Cyrtaucheniidae—consist of 13 genera and 81 described species.

Trapdoor spiders superficially resemble Funnel-webs. However, most Trapdoor spiders are dark-brown, with mottled tonal patterns of leaf-like bands and markings on the dorsal surface of their abdomen,

Left: a Primitive spider (Mygalomorph).
Right: a Modern spider (Araneomorph).

Typical Trapdoor habitat: water provides humidity, sloping ground reduces the risk of a flooded burrow.

whereas the Funnel-webs are generally black without markings.

Some Trapdoor species are brightly coloured, such as the Mouse spiders of the family Actinopodidae, and many have a thick pile of hair covering their body. The majority are medium to large and solidly built. In addition to those species inhabiting coastal and mountain forest regions, Australia has a large and diverse range of arid-zone Trapdoor spiders.

The name 'Trapdoor spider' has caused some confusion over their correct identification, because many species build neither lid nor door to the burrow entrance. Some of the species that do build a lid or a 'trapdoor' use a variety of forms. Arachnologists familiar with the group can identify the genus or even the species by the specific form of lid construction. some lids are shaped like a bath-plug, some are wafer-like and hinged with strong silk, others are very light and curtain-like and these are kept open at night and closed during the day.

Burrows may be up to 1 metre deep, depending on the species and/or terrain. Some are inclined, some are vertical, others are only shallow. Some are constructed with many bends and curves, sometimes branched. Some species line their burrow with silk from top to bottom, others line the burrow entrance only. The silk of most Trapdoor spiders' burrow entrances does not extend far beyond the rim, whereas the silk of Funnel-webs does.

Food for most Trapdoor spiders consists of crickets, moths, beetles, and grasshoppers taken at or near the mouth of the burrow. A few species have evolved clever, inventive ways to thwart unwanted guests from invading their burrows. Some have devised hidden cells, forked underground shafts and false corridors that lead to dead-ends. These protective measures confuse potential predators and sometimes even trap them. In summer, mature male Trapdoors are

A spider with an open burrow must always keep alert.

A lid-plug retreat, typical of *Aganippe berlandi* in arid regions.

discovered wandering about the bushland or garden in their search for females. When a male Trapdoor finds a female of his species, he constructs a small sheet of silk on the ground and ejects his sperm onto it. From here he fills his palps and is ready to fertilise the female. He is often consumed by the female after mating, providing the mother-to-be with valuable protein necessary for healthy eggs. The males that escape may mate successfully with several other females but survive only one breeding season (male Primitive spiders reach maturity in 4-5 years).

Another distinctive characteristic of the Trapdoor spider is its timidity when threatened or cornered. Unlike the aggressive stance adopted by a threatened Funnel-web, the Trapdoor normally reacts by running away or huddling, legs close to its body, and remaining very still in the hope that danger will quickly pass. When provoked further it may show aggression (or a pretence of it, as a defensive gesture) but is not known to be dangerous to humans. Of course, a bite from any aggressive spider should be medically attended to as soon as possible.

MOUSE (STOCKY TRAPDOOR)

Family Actinopodidae

In Australia this family is represented by one genus only, *Missulena*, and eight described species, all of which are medium to large and measure up to 35 mm in body length. These Trapdoor spiders were formerly placed in the family Ctenizidae. Now placed in the family Actinopodidae, they are named Mouse spiders because of the exceptionally deep burrows made by the females. They excavate long oval, subterranean tunnels to at least 1 metre deep. Few spiders dig to such depth. *Missulena occatoria* was described by Walckenar in 1805 and has the distinction of being the first described Australian Mygalomorph.

The female Mouse spiders are large, black-brown, squat creatures, and often have a very wide cephalothorax. The males of certain species are named 'Red-headed Trapdoor spiders' because of their brilliant carapace and chelicerae; they also have a deep gun-metal blue abdomen.

Male Mouse spiders are found wandering about during the day on open ground—especially after rain—in their relentless search for females. Although normally not aggressive, Mouse spiders will attempt to bite if provoked. The bite of the males, in particular, is considered dangerous to humans, although no deaths have been recorded. Mouse spiders are found Australia-wide although most species have a restricted range.

A male Red-headed Mouse (Trapdoor) *Missulena insigne*, Warrumbungle Ranges, NSW.

Their most distinguishing characteristic is the dimorphism between the males and females—in all species of *Missulena* the sexes differ so greatly in shape and colouring that they have been described as distinct species and given different Latin names. However, this confusion has been remedied in recent years. Other distinctive features, making them easy to distinguish from all other Primitive spiders, are their huge chelicerae and their eye formation. The eyes of Mouse spiders are spread right across the anterior carapace, whereas the eyes of all other Primitive spiders are compactly grouped in the centre of the head region.

RED-HEADED MOUSE	*Missulena insigne* (Cambridge 1877)
	insigne = distinguishing decoration or mark

Description. The female and male Mouse spider *Missulena insigne* measures 20 mm and 15 mm in body length, respectively. The male is readily identified by his bright red chelicerae and head region (caput) and gun-metal blue abdomen. The carapace, abdomen and chelicerae of the female are entirely dark, and often uniformly coloured. The male has longer legs and is slimmer than the rather squat short-legged female. The males of both *M. insigne* and the larger *M. occatoria* are perhaps two of Australia's most strikingly coloured Primitive spiders, and their vivid hues always attract attention.
Toxicity. The display of bright red suggests a cautionary warning, but there are no records of the species causing death to humans. Certainly the poison from the bite of a large specimen may cause temporary illness, especially in young children. In Queensland in 1985 a 19-month-old girl was bitten by a male Mouse spider positively identified as *Missulena bradleyi*. The girl lapsed into a coma 15 minutes after being bitten. She was rushed to Toowoomba Hospital where she received two injections of Funnel-web antivenom, two hours apart, during the 12 hours of her coma. She regained consciousness, was kept under close observation for two weeks, and fully recovered her health without any permanent effects.
Distribution. *Missulena insigne* has a wide distribution range mainly because the spiderlings disperse by ballooning. Compared with the Araneomorphs, air ballooning dispersal by Mygalomorphs is rare, and only the genera *Missulena* and *Conothele* are known to transport themselves this way. *M. insigne* occurs in all mainland states of Australia and in New Guinea, but not in Tasmania.
Habitat. The banks of rivers and creeks are usually the favourite homesites of these spiders. The female digs an oval burrow, sometimes to a depth of 1 metre or even more. During winter months the male can be found inland, travelling briskly over the ground in broad daylight in search of a female—particularly after rain when high humidity above ground ensures optimum conditions for the spider's book-lungs. Although the male leads a nomadic life, he sometimes builds himself temporary retreats in the form of shallow burrows, just deep enough to cover his body; more frequently, he crawls beneath a rock or fallen timber until his next spree.
Prey capture. The food of the longer living female consists mainly of insects and spiders, captured close by the burrow entrance at night. She builds her burrow with two entrances, and some species make a lid or door. As with most Primitives, the female Mouse spider lives most of her life in the darkness of her burrow. The bifid burrow entrances are lined with coarse silk and sealed with double doors during daylight.

BROWN TRAPDOOR

Family Idiopidae

In Australia this family consists of eight genera and 66 species. These Trapdoor spiders were formerly placed in the family Ctenizidae. All are medium to large, and at least 30 mm long. The genus *Arbanitis* is typical of the group both in shape and colouring. It is light-brown to dark-brown with faint bands on the abdomen, its labium (ventral mouth plate) is wider than it is long and without serrations, and the cheliceral fangs are smooth on the outside edges. Some species have a rastellum, a digging instrument in the form of a series of short teeth or spines along the basal joints of the fang bases.

The name 'Trapdoor' has caused some confusion because many species build neither lid nor door for the burrow entrance. Their burrows may be as long as 1 metre and either inclined, shallow, or vertical and ending in a retreat chamber. Some are constructed with many bends and curves, sometimes branched, and some species line their burrow with silk.

In summer mature male Trapdoor spiders wander about the bushland or gardens searching for females. When a male finds a female of his species, he constructs a small silk mat on the ground and ejects his sperm onto it. From this mat he fills his papal bulbs (palp tips) and is ready to fertilise the female.

After mating it is not uncommon for the female to consume the male, so that she is supplied with the protein required for healthy eggs. Some males escape and mate successfully with several other females, but do not survive beyond one breeding season as their feeding instinct does not outlast the sexual drive and process of procreation.

Typical Trapdoor habitat: near water, and on sloping ground.

COMMON BROWN TRAPDOOR	*Arbanitis gracilis* (Rainbow and Pulleine 1918)
	gracilis = of plain style and slender build

Description. Generally dark-brown, with a light-brown foliate pattern on the carapace and abdomen. The body length of the female is about 33 mm, the male is about 23 mm. The male is slender, while the female is more solidly built and shorter-legged. The species has short, conical outer-posterior spinnerets. The male is readily distinguished from the female by his bulbous palpal tips, characteristic of all male Primitive spiders.

Toxicity. *Arbanitis gracilis* is not an aggressive species and its bite is considered completely harmless to humans. Common Brown Trapdoors are normally shy and reluctant to stand their ground even when cornered. They often huddle, motionless, waiting for danger to pass. They demonstrate more courage near their homesite, when pouncing on passing prey at night.

Distribution. This species is commonly found during summer in many areas of New South Wales, where it has adapted to parks and surburban gardens now that it has lost its natural habitat to land development. The males in particular are found wandering about exhausted from their amorous adventures, and they often end up as food for other spiders and predatory insects, some entangling themselves in the snares of Redback and Daddy Long-legs.

Habitat. The species prefers to build its burrow in loose soil on the upper banks of streams and creeks, but it is also found on bare ground and moss-covered patches. It constructs a thin wafer-like lid on the burrow entrance, which is normally camouflaged and difficult to

A female Trapdoor, *Arbanitis gracilis*, body length 33 mm.

A male Trapdoor, *Arbanitis gracilis*, body length 23 mm.

The well camouflaged Trapdoor lid of *Arbanitis gracilis*.

find. It prefers conditions that are not too wet and is often found in backyard gardens.

Prey capture. During the night, the female sits at her burrow entrance holding the lid slightly ajar. When an insect approaches within capture range, she throws the lid back, pounces on the prey, crushes it with her strong jaws and drags it below. This action is so quick that you could miss it if you blinked. The door to the burrow is closed during mealtimes.

SYDNEY TRAPDOOR

Misgolis rapax (Rainbow 1914)

rapax = greedy, grasping, ravenous

Description. The species is dark brown, with golden hairs covering the carapace and limbs. The female measures about 35mm and the male about 25 mm in body length. Both are large and solidly built, with blunt, broad spinnerets. The male is readily distinguished from the female by his enormous palps, his apophysis (heavy spine) and his covering of spiny hairs. As for all Primitive males, he is much slimmer than the female.
Toxicity. When threatened, *Misgolas rapax* may show aggression or make a gesture of bravado, but is more likely to run away. The species is not known to be dangerous to humans. The Sydney Trapdoor should not be confused with the Sydney Funnel-web.
Distribution. This species is widely distributed in New South Wales and is found in the Blue Mountains westwards and over 60 km north of Sydney. It is particularly well known in Sydney where males are found wandering about in search of females during summer.
Habitat. *Misgolas rapax* and *Arbanitis gracilis* (Common Brown Trapdoor) often share the same forest environs, but *Misgolas rapax* chooses leaf litter and grass-covered areas, while *Arbanitis gracilis* seems to favour bare or

Typical habitat of the Sydney Trapdoor, *Misgolas rapax*, in clearings and alongside trails near water-ways.

A female Sydney Trapdoor, *Misgolas rapax*, in attack stance.

moss-covered ground. The Sydney Trapdoor excavates a burrow that is about 30 cm deep and usually inclined. Unlike most Trapdoors, all the *Misgolas* normally construct burrows with a simple silk lining and an open entrance. Although they do not build a door, they seal the entrance with a silk curtain during prolonged rains, which helps to keep the burrow dry. Moist to wet forests are generally favoured by *M. rapax* species and it is not uncommon to find their open burrows dotted quite thickly over grassy or litter-covered patches of ground.

Prey capture. Like most Primitive spiders, they rely on the cover of darkness to catch their prey, which they do with their huge prey-crushing fang bases and their pick-axe fangs. Crawling insects that stumble into capture range are quickly dispatched and taken below to devour.

FUNNEL-WEB
Family Hexathelidae
(also Dipluridae and Nemesidae—Funnel-web-like)

Hexathelidae consists of a large number of Funnel-webs—for example, the subfamily Atracinae includes the genus *Atrax* and *Hadronyche*, and Australia has 35 described species. Much confusion has come about because of the use of the name 'Funnel-web'. Their webs, which are rarely funnel-shaped, usually resemble a long, flat tube or sock. At its lower end is a flat purse-like chamber where the spider huddles during most of the day. Only at night does the spider ascend the shaft to wait at the entrance for insects that stumble into capture-range. Usually, two short entrances into the main tube are built to form a Y-shaped silken structure. The Funnel-webs are also sometimes referred to as Purse-web or Wish-bone spiders.

Funnel-webs are usually purple-black or blue-black to ebony-charcoal, but depending upon age or moulting stage, they may be very dark brown. During moulting, the soft cuticle has a white, milky appearance, which slowly changes as melanin interacts with proteins in the process of darkening and pigmentation. As a group, Funnel-webs can be identified by the terminal segment of the longest spinnerets, which is longer than it is wide; by teeth-like serrations on both margins of the fang grooves; by peg-like spines on the labium; and by a strongly curved foveal groove on the carapace.

Identifying a Funnel-web species relies chiefly on

As a creature approaches the funnel-shaped entrance, the Funnel-web *Hadronyche versutus* rears up on her hind legs, forelegs held high and fangs ready to strike.

The wishbone tube retreat of a *Bymainiella* Funnel-web.

finding the sexual mature male in the company of the female. This is because the female has no externally visible genitalia, which makes positive identification extremely difficult. There are records of female tree-dwelling species living up to 20 years or even longer.

Funnel-web spiders are mainly found in the eastern portion of Australia. Since they are all relics of a once prevalent lineage of rainforest spiders, it is not surprising that their distribution in Australia is largely associated with the Great Dividing Range.

Toxicity. All Funnel-webs should be approached with caution. Some species are now known to be among the most dangerous creatures in existence. All are potentially poisonous to humans and are best left alone. The male Sydney Funnel-web, *Atrax robustus*, is perhaps the deadliest spider in the world. It is therefore wise to wear gloves, enclosed footwear, and protective clothing while working in the garden during summer and autumn in regions where you are most likely to encounter them on their amorous adventures.

Some 15 deaths from Funnel-web bites have been attributed to *Atrax robustus* in the last 60 years in Australia. Up until only recent years, this species has borne all the blame for illnesses and deaths caused by Funnel-web bites in Australia. However, research now shows that the female *Hadronyche formidabilis* and *Hadronyche versutus* are also armed with a venom potentially deadly to humans and may also be partly responsible.

BLUE MOUNTAINS FUNNEL-WEB

Hadronyche versutus (Rainbow 1914)

versutus = clever, crafty, sly

Description. This spider is usually mistaken for *Atrax robustus*. Upon closer observation, however, certain features distinguish it from the Sydney Funnel-web. All members of the genus *Hadronyche* have a highly arched or raised head region, and the male's palpal bulbs are bigger and a different shape from those of the male *Atrax robustus*. Also, the spurs are absent on the tibia of the *Hadronyche* male's second pair of legs. In body length, the female is about 32 mm and the male is about 18 mm.

Toxicity. *Hadronyche versutus* is not known to be deadly to humans but it should be treated as dangerous, for it is as toxic as the Sydney Funnel-web. it is not so frequently encountered because it normally inhabits less populated areas.

This Blue Mountains Funnel-web *Hadronyche versutus* provides transport for these *Parasitus* mites clustered on his abdomen.

Typical homesite of the Blue Mountains Funnel-web, *Hadronyche versutus*.

Distribution. Its distribution range appears to be limited to the Blue Mountains of New South Wales, but specimens have been found as far west as Orange and Bathurst and as far east as Sydney.
Habitat. This species retreats under mossy, rotting logs on the forest floor to construct its silk tube burrow, which also serves as a brood chamber.
Prey capture. *H. versutus'* wide range of prey includes insect larvae, earthworms and even small snails—almost any small creature unlucky enough to stumble upon its well hidden burrow entrance.

Retreat entrance of *Hadronyche versutus* in decaying timber in a subtropical rainforest gully.

NORTHERN TREE FUNNEL-WEB	*Hadronyche formidabilis* (Rainbow 1914)
	formidabilis = terrifying

Description. The huge Tree Funnel-web, *Hadronyche formidabilis*, is indeed formidable. It is the largest of all the Funnel-webs—the female reaches 50 mm long when fully grown. The male is more slender, has longer legs and is 35 mm long. The species is very dark brown to black, has huge fang bases, and its size alone should identify it. It is sometimes confused with another smaller tree-dwelling species which is commonly found from the southern suburbs of Sydney to the northern suburbs of Gosford but which is, as yet, undescribed.

The male *Hadronyche formidabilis* is rarely seen but can be clearly distinguished from the male Sydney Funnel-web, *Atrax robustus*. Not only is it much larger, with a raised head region, but the spur on the tibia of the second pair of legs is distinctly blunt, whereas that of the Sydney Funnel-web is distinctly pointed. Also, the intermediate teeth-like serrations of its fang groove extend the full length, whereas on the male *Atrax robustus* they do not.
Toxicity. This spider is considered highly dangerous to humans, particularly small children. People who have been bitten by it have become severely though temporarily ill; in each case it has taken them several days to recover fully. The female is far more dangerous than formerly believed, since the toxicity of her venom is many times greater than that produced by the male. The toxicity of the venom depends on several factors, such as depletion of the venom, the size and maturity of the spider and the spider's degree of agitation at the time of biting. The antivenom used for a Sydney Funnel-web bite is also an effective treatment for the venom of other Funnel-webs.

The first recorded case of a bite from *Hadronyche*

The entrance/exit design typical of the Tree-dwelling Funnel-web *Hadronyche*.

formidabilis was that of a timber-cutter in northern New South Wales in the early 1980s. The timber-cutter, a large man, was taken to hospital. Some hours later he developed violent pains in all his limbs, vomited and perspired profusely, then became semi-comatose for several hours. During this period he was given an injection of the Sydney Funnel-web antivenom. He regained consciousness and two weeks later fully recovered. Since then a few serious cases of Funnel-web bites have been attributed to this species.

Distribution. This species favours mountainous country. It is restricted to northern New South Wales and south-eastern Queensland—the Hunter River Valley appears to be the southern-most limit.

Habitat. This large tree-dwelling spider is normally found in rainforest pockets or heavily timbered forests undisturbed by humans. It builds its bark-covered retreat in tree stumps and living trees and often makes use of cracks in the timber, knot-holes, spongy wood and abandoned wood-boring insect tunnels, such as those made by the large Longicorn beetles and Wood Moth larvae. It has been found by timber-getters as high as 30 m from the ground.

Prey capture. It feeds on a wide assortment of creatures—tree frogs and geckos as well as timber-frequenting insects. When they climb or alight upon the tree-trunk within striking range of its retreat, the spider makes a lightning dash from its silken tube, seizes the prey and quickly drags it back inside. It crushes the creature between its massive chelicerae and administers a liberal dose of poison at the same time.

SYDNEY FUNNEL-WEB

Atrax robustus (Cambridge 1877)

robustus = strong, robust, mature

Description. As with all spiders of the group, the Sydney Funnel-web has large fangs and venom sacs. These fangs fold parallel to one another beneath the head region and, like pocket-knives, fit into fang grooves. The glossy carapace, cephalothorax and limbs are characteristic of Funnel-webs, and so is its abdomen, which is covered with fine, velvety hairs. Although its colouring varies, it is usually a glossy blue-black. The mature female is about 35 mm long; the male is about 25 mm.

Atrax robustus has spiny, solidly built limbs, a compact eye grouping and cuspules on the labium. It is also identified by a row of teeth along the fang groove and a row on its paired claws. The terminal segments of its spinnerets are long and tapered. The male has large palpal bulbs and distinctly pointed spurs on the tibia of the second pair of legs, for fending off attack during the preliminaries to mating.

Toxicity. During the mating season, when the males are searching for females, or when a female is forced from her burrow, an encounter with these spiders can be an awesome experience. Whenever agitated, *Atrax robustus* tries to attack with astonishing ferocity. The venom of the male Sydney Funnel-web contains approximately six times more atraxotoxin than that of the female. Atraxotoxin, produced by Funnel-webs, and tetrodotoxin, produced by the Blue-ringed Octopus, are both neurotoxins—the most dangerous of all toxins found in the animal kingdom. Neurotoxins prevent the brain from transferring electric impulses to other parts of the body. Because the normal passage of signals is blocked, false impulses are triggered, and

A female Sydney Funnel-web, *Atrax robustus*, body length 35 mm.

The natural habitat of the Sydney Funnel-web *Atrax robustus* is on sloping land near water.

The silk tube entrance of the Sydney Funnel-web *Atrax robustus*.

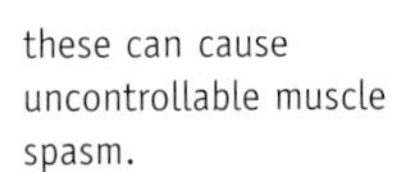

these can cause uncontrollable muscle spasm.

Distribution. Sydney Funnel-webs are dispersed far more widely than once believed. As the clearing of outer rural land continues, whole colonies are forced from their homes and are coming into closer and more frequent contact with humans. Essentially, their range is confined to eastern Australia. They are most widespread in New South Wales, especially along the coast from Newcastle to Nowra, and as far west as Lithgow and Oberon. They are also common in central New South Wales and have even been identified in south-eastern Victoria, transported in rocks, plants or soil.

Habitat. Favourite haunts are lush gullies in wet sclerophyll forests and rainforests, where they construct their retreat tube on the ground beneath rocks and fallen timber. However, they also like moist soil beneath houses, crevices in garden rockeries, and compost heaps in certain areas. The tube may descend below ground for many centimetres in certain sandstone areas offering the stability of high humidity and low temperatures—their ideal environment.

The white silk tube may measure from 20 to 60 cm long, according to the conditions surrounding it. It leads to a purse-like enclosure at its very end, which also serves as a brood chamber. This is the permanent home of the female but the male leaves the tube once he reaches sexual maturity, which takes as long as four years depending upon food supply, weather conditions and local environment. The entrance is normally Y-shaped or T-shaped, so the spider has, in effect, two points of entry or exit. Sometimes the entrance is roughly woven into a funnel shape (more often it is simply round) and braced with numerous struts of strong silk attached to adjacent rocks, tree roots, leaves or twigs. A curtain of densely woven silk is sometimes used for closing the entrance during daylight.

Prey capture. *Atrax robustus* take all their prey at the edge of the 'funnel-web' entrance. Their diet consists of beetles, cockroaches, insect larvae, native land snails and millipedes. Skinks and frogs as well as other small vertebrates are also occasionally taken.

BRUSH-FOOTED TRAPDOOR
Families Barychelidae and Theraphosidae

A male Brush-footed Trapdoor reaches up to 40 mm in body length. Here shown at entrance to female's burrow.

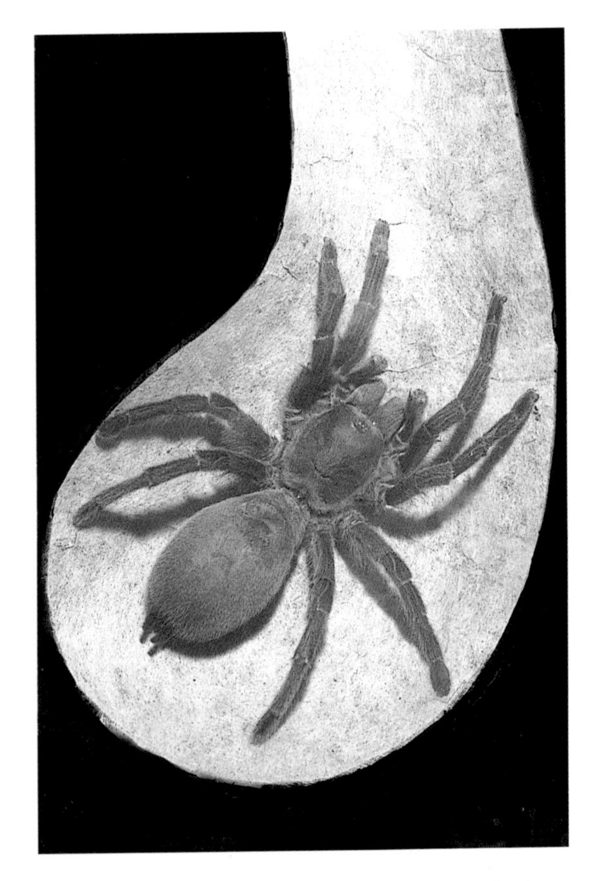

A female Brush-footed Trapdoor can measure up to 50 mm in body length and vary from deep brown to reddish or dusky brown.

Brush-footed Trapdoors seem to be more recently evolved than either the true Trapdoor or the Funnel-web. The Barychelids, however, are more akin to the true Trapdoor than the Theraphosids are.

In Australia, Barychelidae (also known as Barking, Whistling or Bird-eating spiders), consist of four genera and eleven described species. Theraphosidae consist of the three genera—*Selenocosmia*, *Selenotholus* and *Selenotypus*—and seven described species.

Some of the species of the family Theraphosidae are the largest spiders found in Australia. For example, *Selenotypus plumipes* is 60 mm long with a leg span of some 160 mm, and has stout fangs 10 mm long. The two families of Brush-footed Trapdoor spiders differ markedly from one another in both form and lifestyle but they do share the ability to climb smooth, vertical surfaces with ease by means of special claw tufts or brushes on their feet. When these hairs are examined closely under a microscope, they are tooth-edged and rough ended—very similar to certain friction-grip materials used in commercial products. The hairs also work as tiny suction pads due to a film of oil produced from special glands.

The Theraphosidae are also commonly referred to as the Whistling or Barking spiders because they are equipped with a stridulating organ that produces whistling or barking sounds. Only one or two species of the Barychelidae family can produce these sounds. Theraphosids have also evolved the habit of carrying their egg sacs about in the same manner as certain Araneomorphs—the Lycosidae (Wolf spiders). The Barychelidae are generally not as large as the Theraphosids and species range from red-brown, grey, black or dusky-brown. All Barychelids have a velvety covering of fine hair. The Theraphosids are further distinguished from the Barychelids by having long, tapered terminal segments of the outer-posterior spinnerets and a larger, strongly curved fovea (a pit on the carapace for the muscle attachment of the sucking stomach).

Toxicity. The Barychelidae includes certain species that are known to become aggressive when disturbed or cornered, and they will attempt to strike if further provoked. The venom of some species may cause some people temporary illness (aches, chills, vomiting).

The venom of Theraphosidae spiders can cause vomiting, profuse perspiring and pains throughout the body, depending on the health and size of the person bitten. Although the venom is highly toxic in certain species, no deaths from their bite have been recorded. Someone with a strong constitution may experience mild symptoms—swelling at the site of the bite subsides within an hour or two. When provoked or cornered, these spiders often stand their

Mallee scrubland: the habitat of some of the Brushfooted Trapdoor families Theraphosidae and Barychelidae.

Micro-habitat: grass clumps often shelter Primitive spiders.

ground, rearing up in preparation to strike if further threatened.

Distribution. The Barychelidae are widely distributed throughout the interior of the continent, as well as in rainforest coastal regions. Many of the Theraphosidae are arid species, inhabiting the dry land of the interior, west of the Great Dividing Range. However, some inhabit rainforest floors in Queensland, and others are found in the Kimberley Ranges of Western Australia, in the Northern Territory and in New Guinea.

Habitat. Both Barychelidae and Theraphosidae excavate long burrows, often in the upper banks of creeks and streams. They remain deep within their burrows during daylight. The females may live ten years or more, while males complete their lifecycle within five years. However, whereas Barychelids build a lid or door to seal the burrow entrance, the Theraphosids build none. During heavy flooding, spiders of both families avoid drowning because their hairy bodies trap air bubbles that form air pockets around them as they huddle in their burrow.

Prey capture. Barychelids' prey normally consists of frogs and lizards and a wide range of crawling insects. Open range, ground-frequenting Araneomorphs, such as Wolf spiders, are also taken. All prey is captured close to the burrow entrance at night, where the spider patiently sits and waits.

Theraphosidae are notoriously known as Bird-eating spiders. Their reputation for capturing small birds is well founded on reports and verified by observations made by many people over the years. The fledglings and small weak members of ground-frequenting birds are particularly susceptible prey. Frogs, lizards, geckos, large insects and free-roaming spiders are also part of their diet. Most prey is taken close to the burrow. The large, powerful chelicerae crush most prey the moment it is captured. They are nocturnal and remain deep in their burrow during the day. At night, they often leave their burrow in search of prey rather than simply waiting for it to come to them—this can be a long wait.

ARANEOMORPHAE
Modern spiders

A female Huntsman, *Isopeda vasta*.

The Australian Araneomorphs consist of 61 families and 1563 described species. These are the modern two-lunged spiders and include cribellate and non-cribellate spiders—those with a cribellum or 'spinning plate' which produces woolly or hackled silk textures. Their distinctive external features are as follows.

- **Chelicerae:** fang base and fang-tip segments combined. These are aligned vertically beneath the head at 90 degrees from the body.
- **Fang tips:** move independently of each other in diaxial (pincer) action, opposing one another to meet.
- **Palps:** leg-like appendages between the chelicerae and the first pair of legs. These are short compared with those of Primitive spiders.
- **Book-lungs:** in most Modern spiders these are supplemented with a tracheal breathing system, except for the 'lungless' spiders of the family Symphytognathidae.
- **Three pairs of spinnerets:** usually present, with or without the cribellum ('spinning plate') and colulus.
- **Cribellum or colulus:** if present it represents the anterior medium spinnerets. The basal segment of the posterior spinnerets is undivided.
- **Haplogyne or entelegyne vulva:** present in some species (see Glossary of terms).
- **Abdomen:** entirely unsegmented dorsally.

All cribellate spiders construct a form of snare for catching prey. The non-cribellate spiders include those which are either hunters or snare-makers. The earliest snare-making spiders constructed their webs close to the ground and caught crawling and climbing arthropods. As web-making spiders ventured higher to exploit the rising population of climbing and flying insects, numerous spider forms reverted to open-range hunting to exploit the ground litter and rock areas where competition was not so strong.

The only evidence that a cribellum once existed on many of these spiders is a small bump (called a colulus) ahead of the spinnerets, where the cribellum once was. The non-cribellate snare-makers manufacture sticky silk (e.g. wheel-webs) with special silk glands (aggregate glands). The silk is then fed through the posterior spinnerets. The cribellate snare-makers produce a hackled silk from at least three different silk glands. This compound silk is not 'gluey' but adheres to insect prey by electrostatic attraction.

A typical sclerophyll forest habitat for Open-range Hunters such as Wolf, Sac, Huntsman and Jumping spiders.

Most Araneomorphs complete their life-cycle within one or two years. However, exceptions found in arid regions can live several years owing to breeding cycles prolonged by drought and lack of insects.

The International Commission on Zoological Nomenclature aims to stabilise the taxonomic boundaries of Modern spiders. In recent years revisions of the Araneomorphs have resulted in certain subfamilies being promoted to families—for example, Desidae and Metidae— and new families such as Amphinectidae and Palpimanidae have been added. The subfamily Nephilinae may also be promoted, but remains with the Araneidae for the present.

OPEN-RANGE HUNTERS

SAC
Families Clubionidae, Miturgidae and Gnaphosidae

Australian Sac Spiders form 52 genera and 184 described species: Clubionidae has 17 genera and 68 described species, Miturgidae has 3 genera and 20 described species, and Gnaphosidae has 32 genera and 96 described species.

The Sac Spiders are all two-clawed Open-range Hunters, and between the claws are tufts which act as suction pads. These enable them to negotiate smooth vertical and horizontal surfaces such as the underside of shiny leaves, smooth stems or tree trunks with ease. Most have large powerful chelicerae and a body structure generally similar to that of the Wolf spiders. Most Sac spiders are brown or grey to match their surroundings, and have eight eyes in two rows of four. They often make their retreat sac between two leaves sewn together, or underneath flower heads where insect prey is prevalent. Whenever they need to moult, they form a sac to hide in until their new outer skeleton hardens and they can go about their normal duties.

Toxicity. All Sac spiders are aggressive hunters and all build either a temporary or semi-permanent retreat in the form of a silken 'sac', hence their common name. Most can inflict a painful bite with their large chelicerae, so be careful if you investigate the interesting white silken sac, as the occupant will not hesitate to emerge and attack. The bite of some species can cause illness and slow-healing necrotic sores near the site of the bite. Most species are nocturnal and lead a very secluded life during daylight hours.

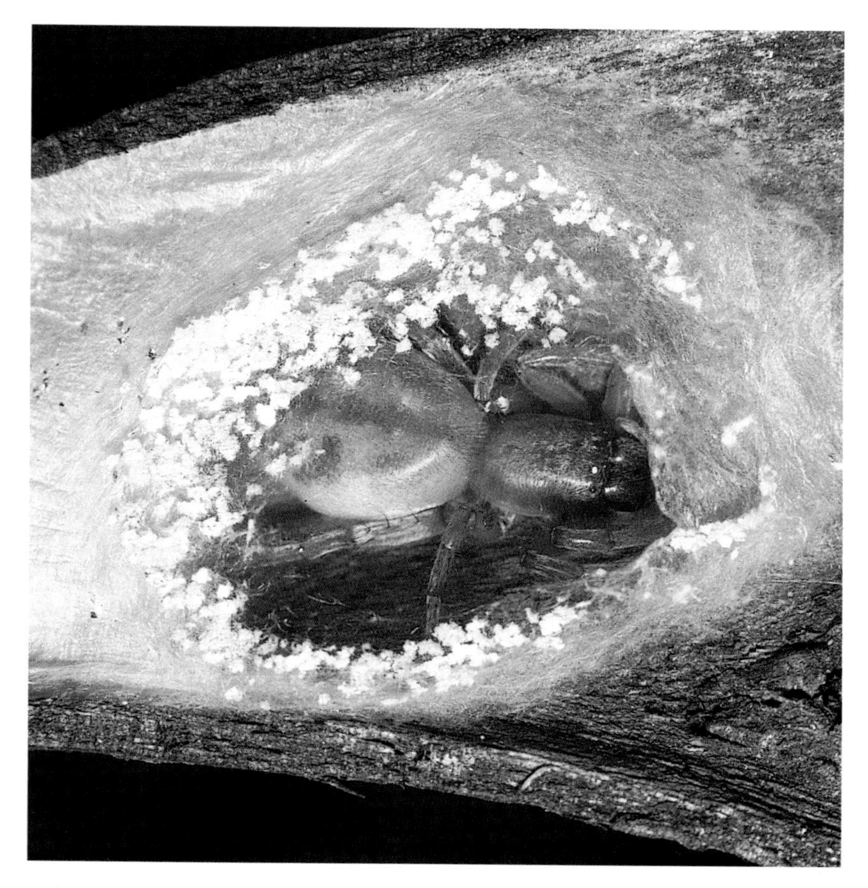

A female Sac, *Clubiona elaphines*, body length 20 mm, a species found in Victoria and Tasmania. Its retreat, normally built under eucalypt bark or leaves is also used as a brood chamber.

BIG-JAWED SAC

Family Clubionidae, Genus *Cheiracanthium*

Description. This genus occurs worldwide, and is especially common in warm countries. *Cheiracanthium mordax* is attracted to houses and seeks out-of-the-way hiding places there during the day. This species measures about 10 mm long, is a semi-translucent buff colour and has long legs, especially the male.

Toxicity. Several species of *Cheiracanthium* can give painful bites, causing headaches, nausea and muscular pains; none are lethal.

Distribution. Several species are found in Eastern Australia, ranging from Victoria to Cape York. Others are found in Tasmania. *Cheiracanthium mordax* is found throughout Australia.

Habitat. These spiders do not build a permanent retreat or shelter but simply hide where they can when not actively hunting. However, they generally construct a silken sac for moulting purposes and, when ready to lay her eggs, the mother-to-be builds a silken brood chamber, into which she seals herself to guard her eggs and hatchlings. Native Clubionids hide among flowers, leaves, bark, leaf litter and grass tussocks, commonly making temporary retreats in the form of silken tubes, sacs or envelopes, which are rolled or folded from grass blades and held in place with strong white silk. The introduced species, *Cheiracanthium mordax*, sometimes enters houses and hides behind pictures, mirrors, cupboards, etc. It comes out late at night to hunt for insects upon walls and ceilings.

Prey capture. Prey is taken at night among the foliage and flowers by these fierce nocturnal open-range

A female Big-jawed Sac, *Cheiracanthium gilvum*, is 10 mm or more in body length. This species is common in NSW and Qld.

hunting spiders. They stalk insects resting or feeding on leaves, branches or tree trunks and on tip-toes above the prey, they suddenly fall directly onto the unsuspecting creature, stilling it quickly with huge chelicerae and swift-acting poison. Beetles, moths, flies and caterpillars form a large proportion of their diet.

LARGE SAC

Family Miturgidae, Genus *Miturga*

Description. Australian Miturgidae has 3 genera and 230 described species which are distinguished from the Clubionidae by their large body size (often up to 25 mm) and by their distinctive body patterns. Also they build semi-permanent shelters, whereas the Clubionids build temporary shelters only.

A typical representative of the family is *Miturga agelenina*, which looks very much like a Wolf spider, both in build and colour patterning, but can be readily distinguished by its forward-projecting eye formation and four creamy-yellow dorsal and ventral stripes on the abdomen. One widely spread species is the Large Sac spider *Miturga lineata*, which is 20 mm in body length. It is grey-brown, with dark-brown lateral stripes on its carapace and four longitudinal dark-brown rows of dots sprinkled with white markings on its abdomen. Rows of white markings on the abdomen's underside distinguish it readily from a Wolf spider. Another widespread Sac spider is *Miturga gilva*, which is red-brown and about 10 mm long.

Toxicity. All of the Miturgids

Large Sac spider *Miturga lineata*. Note the different eye formation to that of Wolf spiders.

are equipped with stout fang bases and are capable of painful bites, which can cause headaches, nausea, vomiting, diarrhoea, muscular pains. None of the family, however, are lethal to humans.

Distribution. A number of species are widespread, ranging from Western Australia, South Australia, Victoria, New South Wales, Queensland and Tasmania. They appear to favour warm temperate zones.

Habitat. Miturgids construct large white silken sacs, usually close to the ground, often beneath rocks, stones and logs. The silk retreat is normally constructed so that it has two openings, and one or the other is used for an entrance and/or an exit. The sac is usually sealed while the female raises her young within. As with all Sac spiders, moulting also takes place inside the sac. Fallen timber and ground litter are among the favourite micro-habitat of these spiders.

Prey capture. Insect prey is either captured as it stumbles too close to the spider's retreat or outpaced and quickly stilled by large powerful chelicerae and swift-acting poison, as with the Wolf Spiders. Spiders and a wide range of climbing, crawling insects are also eaten.

FLATTENED SAC TRIBE

Family Gnaphosidae, Genera *Hemicloea* and *Rebilus*

Description. These are Huntsman-like spiders. Australia's Gnaphosidae has 32 genera and 96 described species, which are distinguished from other Sac spiders by their anterior pair of spinnerets, which are cylindrically tapered and set widely apart. Most species measure under 18 mm long. This family can be separated into two basic tribes: those with a flattened body structure and laterigrade (crablike) legs; and those with a cylindrical body structure and legs more vertical than flat, or fanned so that they raise the body from the substrate.

The flat tribe—those of the genera *Hemicloea* and *Rebilus*—have a flattened body structure similar to that of the Huntsman. This allows them to crawl into very tight crevices between rock slabs and tree bark out of harm's way. *Hemicloea* are distinguished from *Rebilus* by having six spinnerets and more body hair.

Unlike *Hemicloea*, *Rebilus* are territorial in their hunting and do not make silken retreats (sacs). Both genera make the same flattened disc-shaped egg sacs, usually white or grey (depending on their weathering) but *Rebilus* sacs have a smooth surface whereas *Hemicloea* sacs are granulated.

Although their general shape and size are typical of a Huntsman, *Hemicloea* and *Rebilus* are not as hairy. Unlike Huntsmans, they have widely spaced anterior spinnerets, and unlike Huntsman males, *Hemicloea* males are very tiny compared with the females.

Toxicity. While *Hemicloea* and *Rebilus* can be aggressive when disturbed and use their stout chelicerae to give a momentarily painful bite, they are not recorded as dangerous to humans. Their harsh lifestyle has made them highly efficient predators, relying on their speed and huge chelicerae to provide the necessities of survival.

Distribution. Both genera of these Sac spiders appears to have a restricted distribution range and are normally found under stones, bark, rocks and logs in New South Wales and southern Queensland. They also occur among the granite rock outcrops in south-western Australia. I have found them to be common in the Flinders Ranges in South Australia. They favour cooler, drier regions and are

A typical sandstone habitat of the large flat Sacs of the family Gnaphosidae. Sandstone rockeries are their favourite haunts where they hide in tight crevices between rock slabs.

decidedly southern in their range.

Habitat. *Hemicloea* are frequently found beneath loose flat rocks or between crevices in sandstone outcrops. The clearing of sandstone for garden rockeries has made these spiders vanish from many areas. Although *Rebilus* and *Hemicloea* have similar lifestyles, *Rebilus* normally prefer to live behind bark or cracks in granite rocks.

Prey capture. Climbing and flying insects are run down and quickly overpowered by the same method used by Wolf and Huntsman spiders. These Sac spiders remain motionless on the tree trunk or rock until they gauge the striking range. They move with astonishing speed before the creature knows what has happened.

CYLINDRICAL SAC TRIBE

Family Gnaphosidae

Description. The female White-tailed Sac spider, *Lampona cylindrata*, one of the largest of its genus, measures up to 20 mm long, with the slimmer male at 12 mm. It is dark plum to black, depending on its age and when it last moulted. Its legs may be red-brown to black, also depending upon its age—the colouring and patterns darken with successive moults. Its carapace is glossy and pitted. The adult has an outstanding patch of white on the dorsal tip of its abdomen. The juvenile has a double series of light patches on the dorsal surface of the abdomen which deepen with each moult until they disappear, leaving only the distinctive white 'tail'.

Toxicity. Its bite is believed to cause humans severe illness for a short time. Although the portion of venom containing flesh-dissolving enzymes would fit on the head of a pin, the species carries *Mycobacterium ulcerans*, a microscopic organism that can cause necrotic (ulcerous) sores. A vaccine is being developed but needs more funding. Although dangerous, the bite is not lethal. The application of aloe vera and of L-Cystine ointment has in some cases counteracted the necrotic venom.

Distribution. Populations of the species range across Australia, including Tasmania, but mostly in temperate regions, and it is also found in New Zealand.

Habitat. *L. cylindrata* prefers cool places, where it builds a temporary tubular retreat sac, in which it shelters by day. In bushland it can be found beneath flaking eucalypt bark, often close to sheet-web spiders, upon

A female White-tailed spider, *Lampona cylindrata*, body length 20 mm. This species carries *Mycobacterium ulcerans*, and the wound from its bite can become a slow-healing ulcer.

which it preys. In late summer, when it matures, it sometimes wanders into human habitation to escape the heat. There it continues to build retreats and hunt, particularly around picture-rail height, where it is cool. **Prey capture.** The White-tailed spider preys on snare-making spiders, and insects. During the evening it positions itself at the outer edges of a snare and plucks the threads to imitate an ensnared insect. The occupant makes an enthusiastic appearance and is violently seized by the White-tailed spider.

WASP-MIMICKING SAC	Family Gnaphosidae; species *Supunna picta* (L. Koch 1873)
	picta = ornate, tattooed

Description. Even though *S. picta* is a brightly coloured spider, it blends perfectly well with its surroundings. This ground-dwelling vagrant species is also one of the fastest moving spiders in Australia, though it uses only six of its eight legs for running. As a ground frequenting Open-range diurnal Hunter, it moves about at amazing speed especially on bright sunny days, frequently changing direction and stopping at regular intervals to catch its breath, as all fast-moving spiders must do. It waves its pair of forelegs above its body, giving it the appearance of a solitary hunting wasp waving its antennae. At rest, all eight legs are splayed and touch the ground. Its build is like that of the Wolf spider but *S. picta* is readily distinguished by colouring, manner of running and eye formation—two rows of four. **Toxicity.** This spider is reluctant to bite and would

A Wasp-mimicking Sac, *Supunna picta*, 10 mm in body length, and one of Australia's fastest ground-dwelling spiders. It waves its forelegs aloft the way a Solitary Hunting wasp waves its antennae.

rather move away from danger or remain perfectly still when threatened. It is considered entirely harmless to humans.
Distribution. *S. picta* is commonly found in New South Wales and Queensland.
Habitat. It seems to favour sandy clearings with leaf litter and a minimum of plant growth in which to hunt down its prey.
Prey capture. This species is ever on the alert for any small ground-dwelling insects that move into its range of vision, such as small grasshoppers and locusts amongst grasses. It can cover a patch of ground in a few seconds.

WOLF
Family Lycosidae, genus Lycosa

Australian Lycosidae consist of nine genera and 130 described species, most of which make up the genus *Lycosa*. None demonstrate real snare-making skills—all are ground-dwellers and many have burrow retreats. The Wolf spider has remarkable powers of observation—it can recognise landmarks by which it finds its way back home after foraging at night. This orientation skill is due to the fact that its eyes are highly sensitive to polarised light.

The Wolf spider earns its name by its method of hunting and capturing prey—chasing it and running it down as a wild dog does. The most distinguishing features are the eyes and the head region of its carapace, which

A female Wolf spider, family Lycosidae, bearing her egg sac at her shallow burrow entrance at Round Hill Nature Reserve, Euabalong, NSW.

A long-legged Wolf spider *Lycosa* with prey at night. This species has an unusual tendency to leave the ground and climb timber.

A female Little Striped Wolf, *Lycosa furcillata*, body length 8 mm, carrying spiderlings.

Alpine Wolf, *Lycosa musgravei* (body length 30 mm) beside its burrow above the tree-line in the Kosciusko heights.

stands almost vertically against its abdomen. The carapace is commonly patterned in various shades of contrasting colours, often radiating bands, sometimes extending to the abdomen. The feet have three claws but no claw tufts, so the spider cannot negotiate smooth slippery surfaces.

Its tracheal breathing system allows it to be extremely agile by comparison to the slower four-lunged Mygalomorphs. The female Wolf spider drags her spherical egg sac behind her during hunting sprees and carries her young on her back, where they hold onto hairs specially shaped to provide a foothold.

Digging a tunnel is not always necessary. Sometimes a Wolf spider uses the abandoned tunnel of another invertebrate. Holes and tunnels made by cicada nymphs emerging from the soil, or the tunnels of root-feeding Cossid moth larvae are ideal and save the spider a great deal of work. Wolf spiders are perhaps amongst the most versatile and adaptable of all spiders as they are found in just about all climates and situations, from deserts to rainforests.

GARDEN WOLF	*Lycosa godeffroyi* (L. Koch 1877)
	godeffroyi = excellent

Description. A classic representative of its family, *Lycosa godeffroyi* is a large, handsome spider, patterned in shades of orange-brown, grey and black, with grey-brown chevrons and radiating bands on its carapace. The female is 35 mm and the male is 20 mm long.

Toxicity. This is not an aggressive species. However, if handled or molested it can inflict a painful bite and may cause infection and skin lesions. Some people bitten by an unidentified creature while gardening have suspected the Wolf spider of being the villain. No human deaths are attributed to its bite.

Distribution. *L. godeffroyi* is widely distributed throughout New South Wales and across the entire

A Garden Wolf spider leaving her burrow at dusk.

Two Garden Wolf females in combat at dusk on the forest floor.

A Garden Wolf, *Lycosa godeffroyi*, pulverising her prey between powerful chelicerae.

temperate zone of Australia. It is Australia's most common Wolf spider, and inhabits mallee country, grasslands and open woodlands. Though well established in certain areas of bushland, it has also been forced to take up residence in urban backyards if its natural habitat has been destroyed.

Habitat. This spider lives in a burrow without a lid. The entrance is often surrounded by leaf litter or grass woven into a little fence around the rim and lined with silk. It favours open clearings for this burrow and is often found in the home garden. Its grey and brown coloration conceals it well amongst leaf litter. Open woodlands, grasslands and clearings along forest trails are favoured, especially when the soil is a sand and clay mix, which makes excavation easy.

Prey capture. Wolf spiders leave their retreat at dusk to begin their nocturnal activities. They rely upon their keen eyesight, speed and strength for stalking prey, and show great courage in confronting and overpowering large ground-crickets, locusts and other spiders. Unlike Primitive spiders, Wolf spiders are active hunters and do not simply sit and wait at their retreat entrance.

NURSERY-WEB
Family Pisauridae

Australian Pisauridae consist of 10 genera and 25 described species, most of which are placed in the genus *Dolomedes*. Nursery-web spiders favour damp situations at the edges of streams, creeks, ponds and swamps, where they run across the water surface or dive below it after prey. The water may be brackish, running or still.

Nursery-web (or Water) spiders are closely related to the Wolf spiders, and the arrangement of their eyes is perhaps the only feature that distinguishes them. Their eight dark eyes are not large nor placed in square formation like those of the Wolf spiders, but set into two rows of four across the front of the head region. The eyes of the first row are smaller than those of the second.

Their life history is also very different to that of the Wolf spiders. The female Nursery-web spider forms a spherical egg sac like the one that the Wolf spider makes, and carries it about beneath her sternum between her palps and chelicerae. She does not drag the sac from her spinnerets as the Wolf female does. When she is aware that her eggs are about to hatch, she constructs a tough silken nursery or brood chamber (this is how she earns her name) and normally suspends it between reeds and shrubs overhanging the water. During the period when the spiderlings emerge from their eggs, the female becomes aggressive if disturbed.

Toxicity. These spiders are considered harmless to humans, although a bite from a large female may be temporarily painful.

WATER	*Dolomedes australianus* (Koch 1865)
	australianus = southern in origin

Description. This species is typical of the family and one of the most frequently seen spiders inhabiting creeks and streams. The female measures 25 mm or more and the male 20 mm in body length. Both are strikingly patterned, with white and orange-yellow stripes running lengthwise along the carapace and have a

Nursery-web *Dolomedes*, (Water spiders) favour rainforest swamps, ponds and creeks.

A female Nursery-web, *Dolomedes australianus*. Claw tufts enable her to run across water.

long tapering abdomen. The legs are long and tapered and the feet have special hairs for walking on water surfaces. These spiders can move with astonishing swiftness when disturbed and can run and jump across water.

Toxicity. The female can become aggressive during nesting time when she is guarding her young. The bite can be painful, but is not dangerous to humans.

Distribution. *Dolomedes* are common all through Australia, especially in the temperate south-east zone, south-western Australia and Tasmania. Most of the described Nursery-web species have been placed in this genus and it is also particularly well known in Europe.

Habitat. Australian *Dolomedes* are also frequently called 'Water spiders' as they favour forest swamps, ponds and creeks in rainforest gullies. They can walk and run on the water because of the fine hairs on their tarsi, which trap air and act as tiny water buoys. They can also dive beneath water and stay there for long periods. When avoiding danger or the intense heat of summer they descend below water by climbing headfirst down a reed stem or rock until entirely submerged. Here they can wait out lengthy periods, surviving on air bubbles trapped in the hairs surrounding their book-lungs.

Prey capture. Prey includes a wide range of insects including dragonfly and damselfly nymphs, stonefly nymphs and insects that fall into the water, such as moths, beetles, grasshoppers, flies, bees, and cicadas. These spiders are sometimes discovered in suburban garden fish ponds and have been seen eating small goldfish and juvenile tadpoles.

HUNTSMAN
Families Heteropodidae and Selenopidae

Australian Heteropodidae, formerly Sparassidae, consist of 13 genera and 94 described species. Australian Selenopidae consist of only one described species within a single genus: *Selenops australiensis*.

These big spiders are commonly known as Tarantulas or Triantelopes, and are also known as Giant Crab spiders because of their rapid sideways scuttling gait. Huntsmans generally have a somewhat flattened body structure, which allows them to squeeze into cracks and crevices in rocks and timber and under loose bark. Some of the compressed spaces these big spiders can squeeze into have to be seen to be believed. Unlike most spiders' legs, which bend vertically, the Huntsman's long hairy legs spread out laterally, point towards the front and bend towards the rear. All are two-clawed and have claw tufts and scopula beneath their tarsi and metatarsi which enable them to grip smooth, vertical surfaces securely. They have a highly flexible membrane connecting the metatarsus and tarsus, and much longer tarsi than most spiders have, making them sure-footed and extremely agile.

A large Heteropodid may measure 160 mm tarsus to tarsus across outstretched legs. The male is always a little smaller than the female and may be easily recognised by his club-shaped, distinctly bulbous palps. The Selenopidae spiders are smaller (up to 20 mm long) and less common than the Heteropodids. Heteropodids have eight large eyes, set in two rows of four spanning the front of the carapace. Some of the tropical species have their lateral eyes set on raised tubercles, which increases their vision range. The eight eyes of the Selenopids are also set in two rows, but six of them make up the front row, and two median eyes (set behind the front outermost eyes) form the 'second row'.

Two Huntsmans in mortal combat.

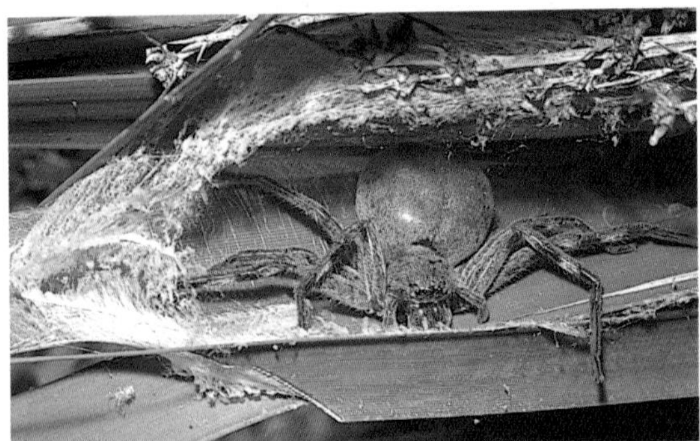

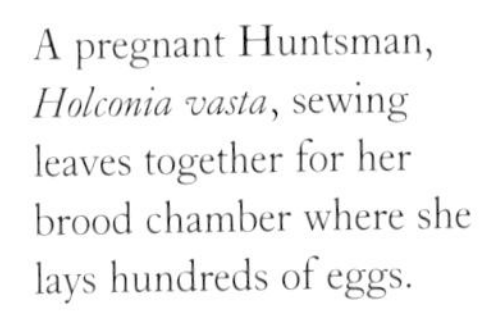

A pregnant Huntsman, *Holconia vasta*, sewing leaves together for her brood chamber where she lays hundreds of eggs.

Huntsman *Holconia* sp. with her newly formed egg sac.

All Huntsman spiders are nocturnal and hunt on foot; none build silken snares of any kind. They are normally found huddled beneath flaking eucalypt bark or dead standing River Oaks which provide ideal shelter. All female Huntsman species have a strong maternal instinct. Once fertilised, the female constructs a brood chamber beneath the bark of trees or uses leaves bound together with silk.

Toxicity. Although a large Huntsman can give a painful bite, most are entirely harmless to humans. Two species of *Neosparassus* can cause brief illness—headaches, chills, muscular pain, vomiting and diarrhoea.

SYDNEY HUNTSMAN	*Holconia immanis* (Koch 1875)
	immanis = enormous, monstrous

Description. This species (formerly named *Isopeda immanis*) is one of Australia's largest Huntsmans. I have come across individuals measuring 45 mm long and 160 mm across outstretched legs. It is immediately distinguished from most other species by its size and its third and fourth pair of legs, which are about half the length of the first and second pairs. The eyes are set in two rows of four, along the front of the carapace. The species is attractively mottled in shades of grey or brown, with a generous sprinkling of white and grey-brown hairs, and there is often a dark stripe running halfway down the dorsal surface of the abdomen beginning at the carapace.

Toxicity. This spider is not considered dangerous to humans, although a large individual can give a painful bite, which I have experienced when handling females guarding their egg sacs in the summer months.

Distribution. The species is most frequently found in

The female Sydney Huntsman *Holconia immanis* can grow to at least 45 mm long.

subtropical and tropical regions of Eastern Australia, form Victoria well up into Queensland. It is common in New South Wales, especially around the Sydney region, which explains its common name. It is also widely distributed in Queensland.
Habitat. This big, speckled-legged species lives under the flaking bark of trees, under large flat rocks, and beneath the fibro and corrugated iron coverings of houses, workshops and garages. Having laterigrade legs and a flattened body structure, it can comfortably squeeze into narrow cracks and crevices. Most of us have come across one of these spiders in the garden, in bushland or inside our house. Uncovering one from behind a curtain or the sun visor of our car can be a startling experience. Remember, though, that the deadly Mygalomorphs cannot climb into ceilings of cars or houses.
Prey capture. A wide range of tree-frequenting, climbing and flying insects are eaten. The adult female Huntsman doesn't hesitate to pursue large insects and can make a lightning-fast dash to surprise an unsuspecting creature milling about the tree trunk. Even though these spiders are essentially nocturnal, they still take advantage of daylight insect populations, such as cicadas feeding on eucalypts and insects gathered at sap-flows. I have seen these spiders venture into broad daylight from behind bark to capture prey, sometimes dragging it behind loose bark, but more often feasting on it on the tree trunk.

RED-BROWN HUNTSMAN

Delena cancerides (Walckenaer 1805)

cancerides = crab-like

Description. This is one of Australia's most common species. It is large, measuring at least 35 mm long. The male is slightly smaller than the female. The species varies in colour but it is usually red-brown or grey-brown, with black-tipped legs (one of its most distinguishing features). Its eyes are set in two rows of four along the front of the carapace, typical of the family. *Delena* bodies are extremely flattened, even more so than those of the *Holconia* species, so they can squeeze into cracks and crevices where other creatures cannot enter.
Toxicity. None of the spiders of this genera are dangerous to humans, but a bite from a

The female Red-brown Huntsman spider *Delena cancerides* (body length 35 mm) is Australia's most common species.

The *Delena* Huntsman has black-tipped legs and chelicerae, and a very flat carapace. The egg sacs here belong to a Sac spider, *Hemicloea*.

Delena cancerides spiderlings and juveniles. This Huntsman species has an unusual tendency to colonise.

large specimen can be painful.

Distribution. These spiders are widely distributed throughout Australia, including Tasmania and small islands off the mainland. However, they are more common in southern regions of the continent.

Habitat. Cracks, crevices and holes in old fenceposts in country areas can yield large populations of these spiders. They are also commonly found under loose bark, beneath rocks and behind iron and fibro on buildings. Unlike most other Huntsman species, which are solitary outside the mating season, *Delena* colonies can consist of hundreds of individuals working and living together to hunt and share shelter.

Prey capture. Red-brown Huntsmans are often found in family groups huddled beneath flaking bark, where generations in various stages of growth intermingle. During the night they come out in search of prey, which includes resting diurnal flying insects and active nocturnal insects that climb on tree trunks and foliage. When dawn breaks, the players of the forest-theatre return backstage until the next evening's performance. Unless you venture out at night carrying a torch to witness the events, you will be none the wiser of what has taken place in the forest or in your own garden.

BADGE HUNTSMAN

Genus *Neosparassus* (formerly *Olios*)

Badge Huntsman spiders (formerly known as *Olios*) are perhaps the most versatile and adaptable of all the Huntsmans, and the most widespread. Yet they fall easy prey to the large, spider-hunting wasps, which seek them in holes around the base of tree-trunks.

Description. Within this genus there are 25 Australian species. Many are extremely colourful. They have blue, yellow, black and white bands and spots on their legs, and often a brilliantly coloured 'badge' design on the ventral surface of their abdomens, with different black and white, orange and yellow markings according to the species.

Although their eyes are set in typical Huntsman formation, Badge spiders are easily recognised by their distinctive dome-shaped carapace, by the rounded abdomen that tapers to a

A female Badge Huntsman, *Neosparassus diana*, body length 25 mm. All *Neosparassus* have an arched carapace and humped, tapering abdomen.

A female Badge Huntsman *Neosparassus punctatus*. The badge design varies with individuals.

point, and by their legs which they hold more vertically than other Huntsmans do, raising the body clear above the substrate. *Neosparassus calligaster* and *N. punctatus* are the only two known species considered dangerous. The female *N. calligaster* measures 25 mm and the male 20 mm in body length. This species is yellow-orchre brown above and the underside has a distinct badge-shaped patch of black and white, sometimes bordered with orange stripes. *N. punctatus* is similar to *N. calligaster*—the female measures up to 30 mm long, the male up to 20 mm long. It is yellow-brown on top, the ventral surface is brightly coloured, and its legs are typically banded.

Toxicity. No deaths have been attributed to their bite but they have been reported to cause illness—usually brief, but severe in some cases, with headaches, chills, muscular pains, vomiting and diarrhoea.

N. calligaster and *N. punctatus* should not be confused with the Badge Spider *N. diana*, which has a distinctive triangular badge marked with orange and surrounded with lemon-yellow. This species is entirely harmless to humans.

Distribution. All the Huntsman spiders of this genus are readily distinguished by their arched carapace and a humped abdomen that tapers to a point. *N. calligaster* occupies both coastal and inland Eastern Australia and is fairly common in the dry sclerophyll forests of New South Wales and Queensland. *N. punctatus* also lives in dry sclerophyll forests, both in coastal and in inland areas of New South Wales and Queensland, but is not as common.

Habitat. *Neosparassus* are all ground-dwellers that hunt their prey at night amongst foliage. A few species live in burrows, much like Wolf spiders of the genus *Lycosa*. Some species prefer to use abandoned burrows made by cicada nymphs, longicorn beetles and wood moths;

others build their own. Since they have no rastellum, they excavate burrows in soft soil around the bases of tree trunks. The burrow entrance has a flanged rim and sometimes a lid, which is camouflaged with sand or soil.

Prey capture. As with all Huntsmans, Badge spiders build no snare, but hunt on foot among foliage at night. Most species are highly adept at climbing, since their claw tufts and brushes function as suction pads on steep, slippery surfaces such as shiny leaves or smooth tree-trunks. If you wish to find these colourful spiders, go out at night in spring and summer with a torch and look among native bushes and shrubs. Your chances are good, as a wide range of insects are captured in the night's adventures.

JUMPING
Family Salticidae

Australian Salticidae consists of 76 genera and 252 described species. Because these spiders are daylight hunters and do not rely on silk snares to capture prey, nature has endowed them with great mobility and keen eyesight.

A Jumping spider advertises its identity the moment it jumps, and a silk anchor is always trailing behind it for safety, in case the spider miscalculates a leap. The name Salticid comes from the Latin word *salto* and means 'to dance with pantomimic gestures'. This is an accurate description of their movements.

Their short stout legs, large median eyes, large

Cosmophasis bitaeniata, body length 7 mm. One of the most colourful tropical Jumping spiders. Its bronze-copper tints change to bright green in sunlight.

Most Jumping spiders are squat, but some are slender like this male *Opisthoncus necator* (body length 14 mm).

Jumping spider with prey. Photo: John Forlonge.

Jumping spider, family Salticidae. Photo: John Forlonge.

Typical habitat of Jumping and Huntsman spiders: Barrington Tops Range, NSW.

chelicerae, and jumping action makes these spiders the easiest of all families to recognise. However, the separation of this exceptionally large family into genera is difficult, even for experts, as there are over 76 genera recognised in Australia alone. None are what you would call big—12 mm in body length is considered large. Most species found in the temperate regions are brown or grey.

Jumping spiders are the only spiders that can jump from a flat surface to a distance of some 20 cm away. This jumping power is supplied by special muscles connecting the leg joints. They also have claw tufts (scopula) which allow them to climb smooth, vertical surfaces with ease. Their eye arrangement also distinguishes Jumping spiders: eight eyes are set into three rows of four, two and two. The first row consists of two very large median eyes flanked by two smaller ones, and this arrangement gives them a 360° scope of vision.

Distribution. Jumping spiders are widely distributed throughout Australia. The greatest number of species are found in the tropical regions of Queensland.

Habitat. Most species are diurnal hunters, and it is not uncommon to see them hunting in the sunlight on the paling fences of suburban gardens. Many species appear to be territorial, claiming a particular bush or tree-trunk.

Toxicity. Interestingly enough, Jumping spiders rarely alarm people, even those who are normally terrified of spiders. These little spiders move about in broad daylight with a confidence not matched by other spiders. Australian Jumping spiders are harmless to humans, with one exception—the Northern Jumping spider, *Mopsus mormon*, found in northern New South Wales and Queensland.

NORTHERN (GREEN) JUMPING

Mopsus mormon (Keyserling 1881)

Description. This species is Australia's largest Jumping spider. The female measures 18 mm and the male 12 mm in body length. The two front pairs of legs of *Mopsus mormon* are robustly developed. Predominantly green, it matches its surroundings, perfectly camouflaged. Colour varies among individuals.

Toxicity. Some people have been bitten by this spider and suffered temporary illness; its bite has been reported to cause painful swelling, sometimes followed by an ulcerous slow-healing sore around the site of the bite, but no deaths have been reported.

Distribution. Its full range of distribution stretches from northern New South Wales and along the coast right to the top of Cape York Peninsula in far north Queensland. I have often observed this species moving about the trunks of coconut palms in bright sunshine hunting for tree-frequenting insects. The spider captures its prey by leaping on it and seizing it with powerful, spiny forelegs, its safety-line preventing a long fall to the ground.

Habitat. The Northern Jumping spider is typically a diurnal hunter, as are most of the family. The female constructs a brood chamber for rearing her young. Broad green leaves and tree trunks are among its favourite hunting sites.

Prey capture. The amazing accuracy with which these spiders pounce on their prey many centimetres away has to be seen to be believed. A fly or grasshopper nymph moves within range, the spider lines up the insect, readies itself, and in a flash the prey is within its grasp. If the spider loses its footing, it usually still manages to seize its prey—its lifeline breaks its fall from the stem or leaf, and

Mopsus mormon is Australia's largest Jumping spider. This female is eating her mate.

spider and prey dangle in mid-air. The spider soon climbs back up its thread. The following three Open-range Hunters—the Spitting, Dysderid and Fiddleback spiders—are introduced European spiders that have made themselves at home in Australia, although they favour the southern parts of the continent. They are not often encountered because they are nocturnal and timid.

SPITTING
Family Scytodidae

Description. The strange Spitting spiders live almost entirely without using silk, except to bind their eggs lightly together as they carry them about between the palps and chelicerae. These spiders are easily recognised by their dome-shaped carapace. The female of the species *Scytodes thoracica* (Latreille 1802) is 7mm long, the male is smaller. Although they have regular spinnerets and abdominal silk glands, they use sticky spittle to capture prey.
Toxicity. *S. thoracica* is entirely harmless to humans.
Distribution. This introduced species from Europe is now widespread in Australia.
Habitat. Spitting spiders are commonly found in homes, where they emerge at night to hunt for moths, cockroaches, flies, silverfish, and crawling insects attracted to lights—on walls, ceilings, and the architraves of windows and doors. However, they are also found in low foliage in gardens or in flower pots on verandahs.
Prey capture. The spittle is made in special glands in the head region and the spider showers it over the insect as it moves into capture range, so that prey is suddenly glued to the spot.

The European Spitting spider *Scytodes thoracica*, supplied for photograph by Eugene Hodgens

DYSDERID
Family Dysderidae

Description. The female of the species *Dysdera crocota* (l. Koch 1839) measures up to 13 mm long, the male about 10 mm. These medium-sized spiders have a salmon-coloured abdomen with smooth red-brown limbs and cephalothorax. They have six eyes, not eight, with two in the first row and four in the row behind.
Toxicity. The bite of *D. crocota* can cause considerable pain and sometimes slow-healing ulcers. No deaths have been attributed to its bite.
Distribution. This European spider has now established itself in Australia (Tasmania and Victoria) and in New Zealand, Japan and America.
Habitat. It normally builds its retreat beneath bricks and rocks, preferring cool, moist haunts. After mating the female constructs a strong silk sac, into which she seals herself until the eggs hatch and the spiderlings are strong enough to make their own way.
Prey capture. The main diet of *D. crocata* is apparently the common little grey slater, *Porcellio scaber*, which lives in large colonies in stable, cool, moist places such as underneath rocks, bricks and fallen timber. During the day the spider keeps to her retreat but at night she ascends to the mouth of her tubular home and waits there, resting her front legs on two or more of the silk trip-lines that radiate from the entrance.

FIDDLE-BACK
Family Loxoscelidae

Description. These spiders are easily recognised by their distinctive fiddle-shaped body. The female of the species *Loxosceles rufescens* (Dufour 1820) is 7.5 mm long, the male about 7 mm. The species is with a flattened body and long limbs. The limbs of the male are longer than those of the female. It looks a little like a cross between a Huntsman and a Wolf spider. Unlike most spiders, this species has six eyes instead of eight.
Toxicity. Even though *L. rufescens* is regarded as dangerous to humans, it is a shy retiring creature and its small fangs rarely puncture an adult human's skin. However, it should be treated with caution as its bite can cause nausea and headaches and, sometimes, an ulcerating lesion that can take weeks or even months to heal. No deaths have been attributed to its bite in Australia, but some have occurred in Europe where this spider is far more common.
Distribution. The species is widespread, and especially well established in New South Wales and South Australia. It prefers cooler regions.
Habitat. *L. rufescens* does not build a home, but lives beneath bark or in dry cool places under rocks and stones. It is also often found hiding behind cupboards in houses, workshops and storerooms.
Prey capture. This vagrant nocturnal hunter does not make a snare. It pounces on crawling insects such as cockroaches, silverfish, beetles and a wide range of small larvae.

AMBUSHERS AND ANGLERS

In Australia, the Ambusher and Angler group of Araneomorphs consists of seven families and 200 described species and represents about 10% of Australia's described spiders. Members of this group do not necessarily have a common origin; they are presented together here because they have adopted a similar method of capturing prey. At some stage in their long evolution they have all changed their habits of either living below ground or relying on snares to catch prey, and have become ambushers or anglers.

They place themselves strategically and wait patiently in the haunts of insects, their colouring merging with their surroundings. As soon as an insect moves within range of capture, they either pounce on it and reel it in with a line of sticky silk, or drop an expandable net of silk over it.

Most of the Ambushers and Anglers group are Crab spiders from the family Thomisidae. Flower and Lobster Pot spiders are in fact types of Crab spiders that have specialised: the former by sitting almost exclusively in flowers; the latter by building a special pot-like structure. Making up the rest of the group are the Triangular, Bird Dung and Bolas spiders, all from the family Araneidae, and the Net-casting spiders from the family Deinopidae.

Few of the Ambushers and Anglers have been studied closely, mainly because they are seldom seen. Ambushers have become keen observers of the ways of crawling, climbing and flying insects, and have developed unfailing patience. They do not appear to register fear and their response to being touched is usually an attempt to discover the cause of disturbance.

Except for the 'bolas' lines of Bolas spiders and the nets of Net-casting spiders, silk used by this group is confined to making eggsacs, safety-lines and brood chambers. Most of these spiders depend upon camouflage and keeping still to secure their prey. Although they frequently change sites, they are essentially sit-and-wait strategists. Flower spiders *Diaea punctata* and *D. variabilis*, for example, lie in ambush on flowers, selecting the petals that best match their own colouring.

The most amazing form of mimicry occur in this group. Many Flower spiders are green, yellow or white, defying detection amongst the flowers and leaves of native shrubs. Other Crab spiders, such as *Amyciaea albomaculata*, mimic ants and wait patiently near their trails to ambush them; *Stephanopis* imitates the rough bark of trees; *Phrynarachne decipiens* and *Sidymella lobata* imitate the fungus and mould of leaf litter. Bird Dung spiders such as *Celaenia kinbergi* and *Archemorus curtulus* imitate the excrement of birds.

Toxicity. Most of the spiders of this group (if not all) can be considered entirely harmless and non-poisonous to humans.

CRAB: FLOWER, BARK AND LOBSTER POT
Family Thomisidae

In Australia this family consists of 27 genera and some 144 described species. The genus *Diaea* represents the Flower spiders here and the species *Saccodamus formivorus* is the only Lobster Pot spider known in Australia.

Description. Most species are 10-15 mm in body length. Knobbly Crab spiders of the genus *Stephanopis* measure about 15 mm, and *Diaea* spiders are 10 mm. Their most distinctive characteristic is that they have two front pairs of legs, which are usually heavier and longer than the hind pairs and are toothed and spiny. Not only do they move like crabs, they also have a crab-like appearance. Males and females are the same shape and colouring but the males are just slightly smaller. Most Crab spiders are easily recognised by their raptorial (strong, spiny) front legs.

All the legs of the spiders in this family are

A female Lobster Pot *Saccodamus formivorus* (body length 8 mm) attaches her silk pot near a Fire-trail ant's nest. It waves its forelimbs to resemble an ant's antennae, and seizes any inquisitive ant that approaches.

A female Elongated Flower spider *Runcinia acuminata*, body length 10 mm.

A female Flower spider *Diaea variabilis*, body length 8 mm.

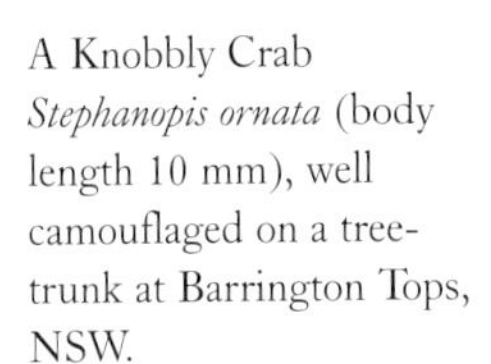

A Knobbly Crab *Stephanopis ornata* (body length 10 mm), well camouflaged on a tree-trunk at Barrington Tops, NSW.

two-clawed and the claw tufts are absent on some species. Their eight eyes are set into two rows of four, spaced across the front of the carapace and often set on small raised tubercles, giving them a 360 degree scope of vision. The Knobbly Crab spiders of the genus *Stephanopis* are so well camouflaged against the background of tree bark and rocks that they escape all but the closest scrutiny.

Toxicity. Not one member of this large family is harmful to humans, nor do any members demonstate any form of aggressive behaviour when disturbed. They often simply drop over the edge of the petal or leaf on their safety-line and ascend again when they feel that danger has passed by.

Distribution.
Representatives occur in New South Wales and Queensland, predominantly in tropical and subtropical regions. Flower spiders of the genus *Diaea* are most commonly found throughout eastern Australia.

Habitat. Flower spiders lie in wait on flowers and are particularly common on native shrubs such as *Grevillea*. They are territorial and often remain sitting on a particular flower-head until the petals wilt, and then simply take up residence on a fresh bloom. Only one spider occupies a flower, unless the two sexes have come together for mating. All *Diaea* spiders are diurnal and hide under petals or leaves at night or hang in mid-air from a single strand of silk to protect themselves from other predators while they rest. This is also a common tactic of Jumping spiders. None build a permanent shelter, but during the breeding season the females build themselves a brood chamber by carefully folding and binding leaves or grass together with silk.

Prey capture. Flies, bees, beetles and butterflies visiting the flowers during the day are promptly seized by the spider's waiting outstretched spiny limbs, which close over the insect like a vice. The prey is usually bitten on the back of the neck and eaten on the spot. Most Crab spiders feed on a wide range of insects and live under leaves and tree bark—some species live out their whole lives beneath loose bark.

TRIANGULAR
Family Araneidae, genus *Arcys*

Australia's largest family of spiders, Araneidae, consists of 36 genera and 340 described species. All, except for some of the following Ambushers and Anglers, belong to the Master Weavers group and make the most refined webs of all spiders.

At least nine species are described for Australia, and *Arcys lancearius* (Walckenaer 1837) is the most common. Triangular spiders ambush their prey in the same manner as the Flower spiders: they pounce upon passing insects and hold them in a vice-like grip with their raptorial pairs of spiky forelegs. Triangular spiders use silk only for their egg sacs and safety-lines.

Description. These showy little spiders are placed in the same family as the Wheel-web Weavers because of their body structure, which is somewhat disguised by their unusual shape and brilliant colouring. However, their lifestyle is far more akin to that of the Crab and Flower spiders, as they build no silken snare at all. A Triangular spider's most distinctive feature is its brightly coloured, triangular abdomen and its glossy surface, carapace and legs. Their vivid colours, when seen in their natural habitat, serve as cryptic camouflage, merging with the various shades of leaf colours. The body colouring of *Arcys lancearius*, for example, is strikingly patterned with yellow splotches and white spots and splashes, outlined in black and surrounded by red and orange. The bodies and limbs of Triangular spiders are almost completely devoid of hair.

Toxicity. All members of the *Arcys* genus are entirely harmless to humans.

Distribution. *Arcys* is found mainly along the east coast and in southern regions. New South Wales and Queensland yield most species. *Arcys lancearius* has a wide distribution range and has been recorded in Tasmania, Victoria, New South Wales, Queensland and New Guinea.

Habitat. Triangular spiders can be found lying in wait upon leaves, seed-heads of grasses and flowers, day or night. They mainly inhabit eucalypt forests and can be found on young trees and regrowth after bushfires as well as on bracken fern in clearings along forest tracks.

Prey capture. The species *Arcys lancearius* patiently waits, holding its raptorial legs high and widely separated, in anticipation of passing insects. The instant an insect crawls or alights upon the leaf or stem, the spider makes a well-calculated pounce, grasps the insect firmly between its spiny forelegs, and usually eats it immediately.

A female Triangular, *Arcys lancearius*, body length 9 mm.

BIRD-DUNG
Family Araneidae, genus *Celaenia*

These spiders are truly remarkable and named for their striking resemblance to bird droppings, since they have blotchy, lumpy bodies. This convincing daytime camouflage can defy detection.

Australia has at least four described species of these remarkable spiders: *Celaenia distincta*, *C. atkinsoni*, *C. dubia* and *C. kinbergi*. It is usually their egg sacs, strung together and fully exposed to the elements among shrubbery, which give away the spiders' position in their daylight repose.

ORCHARD OR DEATH'S HEAD	*Celaenia kinbergi* (Thorell 1868)
	Celaenia = a harpy, cruel and grasping

Description. This species is also referred to as the Orchard spider or Death's Head spider and has a leathery, nodular abdomen that is brown, cream, white and black and perfectly imitates bird faeces. Even when compared to the remarkable camouflages of many of the Crab spiders, the species belonging to this genus have unparalleled camouflage. The female *C. kinbergi* can measure up to 20 mm in body length during pregnancy but is normally about 12 mm, while the tiny male measures a mere 3 mm.

A female Bird-dung (Orchard) spider *Celaenia kinbergi*.

Toxicity. All these spiders are entirely harmless to humans and even when prodded they merely move slowly out of harm's way or remain as still as possible to make the most of their mimicry.
Distribution. *Celaenia kinbergi* is widely distributed across the southern portion of the continent and is found in south-east and south-west Australia, Queensland, New South Wales, Victoria, South Australia and Tasmania.
Habitat. This species often inhabits orchards in New South Wales. Also, on more than one occasion I have observed it on conifers such as pines and fir trees. It frequently lives amongst plants not native to Australia, some of which bear fruit or cones of a size, shape and colouring similar to the egg sacs. The complete lifecycle of this genus is yet to be fully studied and understood.
Prey capture. The Bird-dung spider rarely stirs during the day, but by night its special abdominal glands exude pheromones specifically attractive to male Noctuid moths of the species *Cirphis unipuncta* and *Periphyra sanguinipuncta*. The moth, mistaking the scent for that of his intended mate, flies to the source of the fatal attraction. It flies in ever-tightening circles, actually brushing the spider's body. Suddenly it is grabbed and crushed by stout spiny legs and consumed on the spot. It is interesting to speculate how this spider would survive if the male moths became unavailable.
Even more interesting is that juvenile Bird-dung spiders build miniature conventional wheel-webs for catching tiny prey, until they reach maturity and can produce moth-attracting pheromones. They then abandon their snare-building to take up ambushing.

SMALL BIRD-DUNG	*Archemorus curtulus* (Simon 1893)
	archemorus = original and foolish

Description. Much less common are these unusual little spiders, which share the same protection from predators as the larger Bird-dung spiders do. The female *Archemorus curtulus* measures about 8 mm long and the male is about 5 mm. The colouring of this species combines black and white with various shades of brown, red and yellow. Several *Archemorus* are awaiting description.

Toxicity. All Bird-dung spiders are entirely harmless to humans and make no attempt whatsoever to bite or show aggression when disturbed.

Distribution. This species is widespread in eastern Australia and found also in Victoria, New South Wales and Queensland.

Habitat. *Archemorus curtulus* is usually found amongst exposed leaves, bark and flower spikes in open woodland and forests.

Prey capture. The little Bird-dung Mimicking spider ambushes its insect prey just as Triangular and Crab spiders do, except that it draws up its legs close to its body while it waits, motionless. As an unwary insect climbs or alights closer, the spider suddenly springs forth to seize its prey in a vice-like grip of spiny forelegs.

A female Bird-dung Mimicking spider *Archemorus curtulus*, body length 8 mm.

BOLAS
Family Araneidae, genera *Ordgarius* and *Cladomelea*

Bolas spiders are closely related to the Master Weavers and especially to the genus *Eriophora*. However, they have discarded the wheel-web snare entirely and have evolved highly sophisticated techniques for catching insect prey. They not only use pheromones to lure males moths, as *Celaenia* do, but also use weighted sticky 'fishing lines' which they swing to 'hook' male Noctuid moths.

MAGNIFICENT

Ordgarius magnificus (Rainbow 1897)

The female Magnificent spider is extremely interesting because, unlike the Bird Dung female which relies on its wheel-web snare in the juvenile stage and exudes pheromones only when reaching sexual maturity, she has evolved prey-attracting scents for each one of her stages of growth. There is a perfume to lure certain small species of male moths when she is a juvenile, another for larger species when she has grown bigger, and still another when she attains sexual maturity. The pheromones are selectively used throughout the season as some of the moth species complete their lifecycle and become unavailable.

Description. The female *Ordgarius magnificus* (formerly *Dicrostichus magnificus*) measures about 14 mm long (or up to 25 mm when pregnant) and the male is tiny—a mere 1.5 mm. The species is basically white, except that its abdomen has two bright yellow nodules and numerous tiny, salmon-coloured, star-shaped patterns. The body and limbs are covered with fine hairs that are particularly long on the forelegs.

Toxicity. All these beautiful spiders are entirely harmless to humans and do not display aggression when uncovered from their daylight repose.

Distribution. *O. magnificus* is found in New South Wales and Queensland, and another common species—*O. furcatus*—occurs in Tasmania, South Australia, Victoria, New South Wales and Queensland.

Habitat. During the day, this spider hides in a retreat made of leaves bound with silk, and close by or just above the retreat hang her large, often conspicuous egg sacs. Bolas spiders live amongst the foliage of native trees and shrubs such as the eucalypts, usually a couple of metres from the ground. They can be found in wet or dry sclerophyll forests but *O. magnificus* has adapted remarkably well to urban situations.

Prey capture. The Bolas spider is nocturnal and during the evening the female readies herself for prey by hanging from a horizontal silk thread and dangling a sticky thread from an outstretched front leg tip. The dangling thread is still attached to her spinnerets but controlled by her long front leg, between her claws, from where she plays it out at the appropriate times. This 'fishing tackle' can measure up to 70 mm long and several liquid-gum beads each about the size of a pinhead are suspended along its length. The thread is then weighted with one particularly large, extremely sticky globule at its end. When all is prepared, the spider holds the thread steady and waits. Sooner or later a male moth is attracted by her pheromones and flies in close to investigate. The moth flutters all about the spider, which remains perfectly still and exudes more perfume. Once the moth is within 'fishing' range, the spider lifts her weighted line and begins to whirl it around her. As the insect moves within range, it is 'clobbered' by the sticky globules of the bolas line. The globule sticks fast, the moth is caught—but not yet landed. The elasticity of the line is like a fisherman's split-cane rod. The 'hooked' moth attempts to fly away, is drawn in, goes out again and finally, exhausted by its struggling, is reeled in and gaffed by the sharp fangs of the skilful spider.

NET-CASTING
Family Deinopidae, genera *Deinopis* and *Menneus*

These very unusual spiders are grouped here with the Ambushers and Anglers but they would be equally at home with the Apprentice Weavers, since they combine snare-making skills with ambushing methods. They have several popular names, including 'Ogre-faced'. Representing the family in Australia are 14 described species from two genera: *Deinopis* and *Menneus*. There are nine described species of Deinopids, and the most common are *D. subrufa* and *D. bicornis*. *Deinopis* are easily distinguished from *Menneus* spiders: they have two enormous eyes that stare straight ahead, whereas *Menneus* spiders do not.

The Net-casting *Deinopis ravidus* is sometimes called Ogre-faced.

STICK	*Deinopis subrufa* (L. Koch 1879)
	subrufa = ginger-haired

Description. This species is sometimes called the Stick spider because it looks just like a small clump of twigs or dried leaves and remains perfectly still during daylight. It can be difficult to detect among the foliage. It is the largest of the genus: the female is about 25 mm long and the male is about 12 mm. It is a bright

A typical habitat of Net-casting spiders.

Net-casting *Deinopsis ravidus* weaving at night.

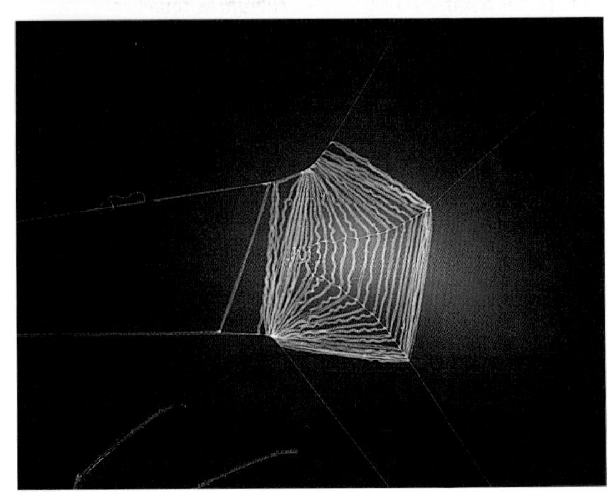

The blue tint is typical of all cribellate webs.

When the Net-casting *Deinopis subrufa* rests during the day it looks like dry twigs. Photo: Eugene Hodgens.

rusty-brown with two distinct humps set midway, dorsally on the abdomen. This spider holds its long, stick-like legs together in pairs when at rest, giving a first impression of having only four legs. The male is very slender compared with the female, and his large bulbous palps accentuate his slenderness.

Toxicity. The Net-casting spider may bite if handled or molested, but is entirely harmless to humans. When threatened, it usually drops on its safety-line or moves quickly away to another twig or clump of leaves, and its cryptic camouflage can make it seem to disappear.

Distribution. *Deinopis subrufa* is found in Tasmania, Victoria, New South Wales and Queensland.

Habitat. This spider bears such a likeness to its surroundings that it is seldom seen. However, once disturbed, it moves away gracefully on its long legs, swinging from one leaf or grass-blade to another with remarkable agility. Upon finding a quiet location, it resumes an almost motionless pose, and with its head down it completely blends in with the plantlife. By carefully searching amongst bushes, shrubs and tall grasses in cool, dry sheltered locations along streams and creeks, or among rock shelters, you may find, a Net-casting spider. Undisturbed areas of grasses and shrubs growing against paling fences and suburban ferneries are also favoured.

Prey capture. Most snare-making spiders simply wait for an insect to become entangled, but the Net-casting spider has evolved a unique net-making technique. It begins to stir at dusk to take full advantage of the most active hours of night-flying insects. Before the spider weaves its net-snare, it makes a simple, rectangular frame from dry silk, with horizontal threads supporting it. Then a ribbon of cribellate silk is laid across the frame in zig-zag fashion. This silk is very adhesive and elastic and is formed of innumerable tiny coils. The elasticity of the net allows it to stretch several times further than its relaxed dimensions.

The spider achieves this amazing engineering feat by moving its nimble rear legs one after the other to comb out the transverse rows of cribellate silk. These legs are equipped with a calamistrum, which combs out the silk as it is drawn from the cribellum. Once the net (the size of a small postage stamp) is completed the spider picks up the four corners with its first, second and third pairs of legs. It holds them apart and raised high to support the net frame while it hangs upside down waiting for prey. When an insect moves into netting range, the spider moves with amazing agility and speed, springing forward and throwing the expanded net over it. It wraps the insect in bands of silk and bites it to stop its struggles. Prey is usually removed from the net later and hung close by. When the night activity quietens down the spider consumes it.

APPRENTICE WEAVERS

In Australia this group consists of 20 families, 99 genera and 270 described species. They represent about 14% of Australian spiders and include the group that has pioneered silk-weaving to make snares, often well above the ground and anchored to plants and rocks, and has diversified according to various niches.

A typical micro-habitat for Apprentice Weavers. Here a cribellate sheet-web snare is strung between wild ginger plants which attract insects.

Apprentice Weaver snares are usually three-dimensional and come in many designs. They not only catch flying insects but also give some protection from predators. Unlike the Mygalomorphs and most Open-range Hunters, these spiders do not overreact to every movement but investigate situations to avoid contact with dangerous prey, and weave their ingenious snares amidst the favourite haunts of climbing and flying insects. Although silk is used for snare-making only minimally by the previously described groups, Apprentice Weavers make copious use of it. Depending on the species, their snares may be tangled web designs, gumfooted, sheet webs, lace webs or unrefined wheel-webs.

All members of this group have three claws without tufts and most have eight eyes set into two rows of four. Their earliest forms of snare construction are associated with the modification of the first pair of spinnerets which have become fused into a spinning plate, the cribellum. Cribellate silk has a distinctive blue tint and is woolly and teased. Insect prey is not ensnared so much by sticky threads as by electrostatic attraction and entanglement.

Apprentice Weavers represent the group of spiders that pioneered silk-weaving to make snares. As the insect population developed the power of flight during the Carboniferous and Permian periods hundreds of millions of years ago, numerous spider forms moved up from the ground onto rocks and plants to extend their use of silk in the capture of climbing and flying insects. These snares are usually three-dimensional, unlike the more sophisticated two-dimensional 'wheel' snares of the more advanced Master Weavers, and are made in many different designs. They not only catch prey but also protect the spiders from predators.

Lace-webs. The cribellate Lace-web spiders are represented in Australia by several common species of the families Amaurobiidae, Desidae, Dictynidae and Oecobiidae. Black House spiders are well known and are often found at the corners of windowpanes. Their snares consist of a series of radiating threads with zig-zag threads crossing between them like the rungs of a ladder, and they are usually heavily embroidered.

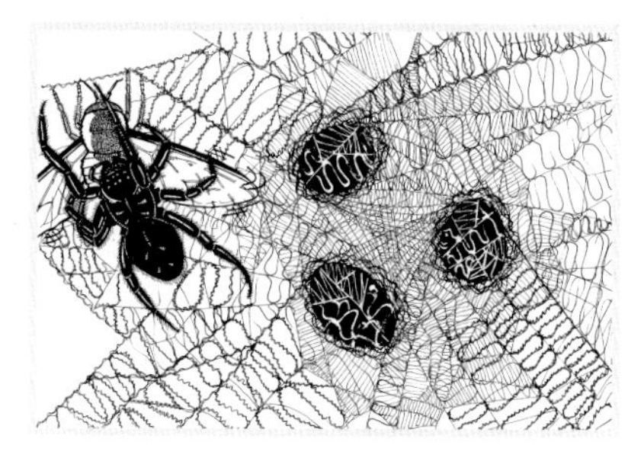

Lace-web of Black House spider *Badumna insignis*.

Because Lace-webs normally build funnel-shaped retreat tubes, they are sometimes confused with Funnel-webs. However, when they are examined side by side, the differences in anatomy become obvious. Besides being Modern spiders with lifestyles vastly different to those of Primitive spiders, Lace-webs have a very different body structure. They are all nocturnal and venture out from their retreat tunnels to make repairs, capture, feed, and mate.

Lattice-webs. Lattice-webs are made by the families Agelenidae, Linyphidae and Stiphidiidae, all of which are non-cribellate spiders. The dry threads of these snares hold prey only long enough for the spiders to rush out and immediately bite it, so Lattice-webs have to be most alert to the arrival of prey. A lattice sheet snare is a finely woven sheet of silk pulled into shapes that vary with the species. It is built under overhanging rocks, roofs of shallow caves, tree trunks or hollow tree stumps, and catches insects that fall or fly into its numerous supporting struts and guylines.

Lattice-web/Platform-web, e.g. families Agelenidae, Linyphiidae.

Lattice sheet-web, e.g. family Linyphiidae.

Platform or crinoline webs. Platform webs are basically lattice webs shaped into specific designs such as the crinoline or hammock web. Lattice-web spiders are represented in Australia by the family Stiphidiidae, which consists of 6 genera and 12 described species. The species *Stiphidium facetum* is the most common and builds an attractive and delicate horizontal snare with a funnel in the centre leading up to the spider's retreat. It is from this shape that the spider gets one of its names, 'Crinoline'—a hooped petticoat or skirt.

The platform lattice-web snare consists of a finely woven horizontal sheet. Its shape depends on the species.

Climbing insects are captured as they stumble into the net. The spider then rushes down immediately to stake its claim. The lattice-work is closely woven, and aged or weathered webs are often opaque.

Tangle-webs. Spiders from the families Pholcidae and Theridiidae use 'scattered silk' (so called because of its seeming disorder) to make what is popularly referred to as 'tangled webs'. In Australia the family Pholcidae consists of 9 genera and 12 described species. The threads are not hung as randomly as they appear; a definite structure is discernible and different constructions are specific to certain species. Tangle-webs consist of a mass of dry silk supported by struts of strong, taut threads, with numerous guylines crossing one another in all directions. The tangled webs of Daddy Long-legs spiders in corners, ceilings, walls and behind furniture are the most common. The tangled threads hold the prey just long enough for the spider to rush forth, wrap it in silk and bite it.

Gum-footed webs. Some tangle-webs have evolved to become 'Spring-trap webs' or 'Gum-footed snares', typical of the Redback spider and are made by family Theridiidae, represented in Australia by some 20 genera and 90 described species. The spider rests upside down in its retreat above the snare. Taut, gum-footed threads or trap-lines stretch from the tangle-web to the substrate below, and stretch like elastic when contacted by prey. The attachment point at the sticky base is designed to snap

A close relative of the Red-back: Red-and-Black spider, *Nicodamus bicolor*.

Gum-footed tangle-web, e.g. family Theridiidae.

suddenly and suspend the prey in mid-air. The struggling insect kicks about and soon finds itself stuck to adjacent threads, which in turn also break off at their base and the spider pulls it in, a helpless captive. Certain Theridiids have abandoned snare-building, and trap prey with a single, sticky spring-trap line.

Unrefined wheel-webs. These are built by the Feather-footed spiders of the family Uloboridae which, in Australia, consists of 6 genera and 13 described species. The most unusual feature of these spiders is that they have no poison sacs. To immobilise their prey, they rely entirely on wrapping it in bundles of silk. Like the Master Weavers, the Uloborids build wheel-webs, but unlike the Master Weavers they have a cribellum and a calimistrum, and their blue-tinted silk is cribellate. Uloborid snares are usually built on an incline, but some are horizontal. They represent the most advanced forms of web designs of cribellate spiders and a parallel evolution has occurred between the two groups. Unlike the beaded, sticky spiral web of Master Weavers, the Uloborid Wheel-web usually has sections of capture threads missing from it. The web is composed of two strands of dry silk which are then coated with sticky silk.

Unrefined wheel-web, e.g. family Uloboridae.

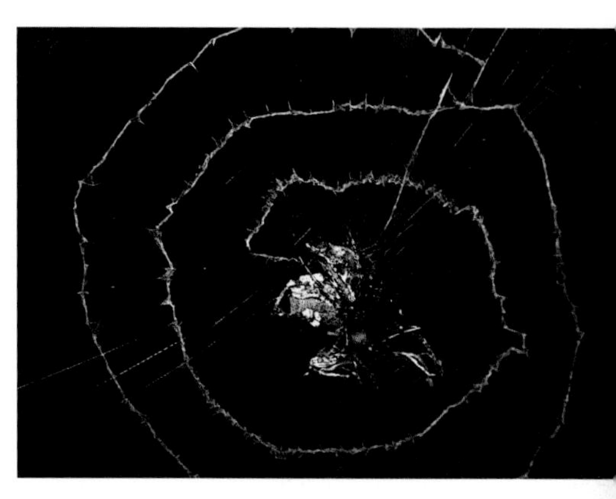

The Apprentice Weavers represent a group of spiders that pioneered wheel-weaving. Some make clumsy snares; others (Master Weavers) have developed marvellous two-dimensional wheel-webs.

LACE-WEB
Family Desidae

BLACK HOUSE OR WINDOW	*Badumna insignis* (L. Koch 1872; formerly *Ixeuticus robustus*)
	insignis = conspicuous

Description. The female is of medium size, measuring up to 18 mm long; the male is only 9 mm. This spider has a robust build and is coal-black or dark brown. The small House spider *Badumna longinqua* is a similar but smaller lighter-coloured species. Some individuals have a faint chevron pattern on the abdomen.

Toxicity. The bite of *Badumna insignis* is poisonous but not lethal. Certain people bitten by this spider have experienced severe pain around the site of the bite, heavy perspiring, muscular pains and sometimes vomiting, but effects are temporary. *Badumna longinqua* may cause similar but less severe symptoms.

Distribution. *B. insignis* likes dry temperate situations and is widely distributed throughout Australia, including Tasmania, but is more common inland. *B. longinqua* is more commonly found inside houses in Victoria and New South Wales along the coast. This smaller species is also found in Tasmania and New Zealand.

Habitat. Loose tree bark, hollow branches and rock crevices are the common haunts of these spiders. They are a familiar sight around our homes and gardens. *B. insignis* often constructs its funnel-shaped lace web in the corner of a window, to exploit insects' attraction to light, or in cracks in fibro, rusting

A female Large Black House spider *Badumna insignis*. Below it is a Noctuid moth's silk cocoon.

A cribellate lace-web snare made by a Desidae spider. The capture threads are strung zig-zag between dry support lines in a series of ladder-like structures anchored above and below the retreat.

Male and female Small Black House spiders *Badumna longinqua* sharing a retreat tunnel.

corrugated iron, ventilators, holes in brickwork, and other places commonly frequented by insects.

Out in the natural bushland, unhealthy trees are attacked by wood-boring insects, such as longicorn beetles and wood moths, and *B. insignis* often builds its snare in such timber because the sap flows caused by boring insects attract a throng of insects such as flies, beetles, butterflies, bees and ants. Any site frequented by insects is a likely hunting-ground for these spiders. They are frequently attacked and devoured by the White-tailed spider *Lampona cylindrata*.

Prey capture. The Black House spider can be observed resting in a corner of its snare or in the retreat tunnel, with forelegs stretched out along the web. Immediately an insect entangles itself, the spider receives the vibrations through sensory hairs set in sockets on its forelegs (the trichobothia). The spider grasps the threads of the snare with its claws and tugs sharply at rapid intervals in a reflex action produced by the femoral muscles. This tugging action further entangles the struggling insect, which is swathed in silk, bitten, dragged into the funnel and consumed in safety. There is always the risk of an Ichneumon wasp or a Spider-hunting wasp looking for an opportunity to attack the spider when prey entices it from its retreat tunnel.

LATTICE-WEB
Family Stiphidiidae

CRINOLINE OR SOMBRERO (Platform)	*Stiphidium facetum* (E. Simon 1902)
	facetum = going away, retiring

This species builds a delicate horizontal web with a funnel in its centre leading up to the retreat where the spider rests above it, upside down.

Description. The spider is light brown to yellow, with dark brown bands or flecks on its long legs. Its eight eyes are set in two rows of four. The carapace is circular and flat; the abdomen is attractively marked and also flattened. Both the male and female measure about 10 mm long, but the male has longer legs and is much slimmer.

Toxicity. *S. facetum* is considered completely harmless to humans. Should you disturb the spider, it will more than likely leap out and suspend itself from its safety-line and haul itself back up again when it gauges that danger has passed.

Distribution. This species is commonly found along the east coast. Its range of distribution is eastern Australia and New Zealand and includes Tasmania, New South Wales and southern Queensland.

Habitat. This spider normally builds its snare under overhanging rocks or on the roofs of shallow caves, on tree trunks or in hollow trees. It is usually found huddled into a cosy crevice or indentation directly above its snare. The lacework is fine, closely woven and often opaque, especially if aged or weathered.

The spider is sometimes difficult to see because its cryptic colouring merges with the rock face. Pirate spiders of the family Mimetidae are often found close to the snares of Platform spiders.

Prey capture. The horizontal web spreads out like a hammock and is intricately woven and supported by three hollow columns which flow into the main web below. A funnel leads to the ceiling where the spider waits, upside down. The sheet is usually built about 30 mm below the ceiling. When an insect falls onto the hammock, the spider runs towards it from beneath the net and bites it through the silk sheet, minimising any risk to itself. The insect is then hauled through to the underside, swathed in silk and hung above the snare to be consumed at the first opportunity.

Sombrero spiders often make their attractive webs under rock ledges.

TANGLE-WEB
Family Pholcidae

DADDY LONG-LEGS *Pholcus phalangoides* (Fuesslin 1775)

Description. The female Daddy Long-legs measures about 9 mm, the male is slightly smaller and rounder. The legs of these spiders are certainly their most distinguishing and unmistakable feature. Some species are marked in subtle patterns and delicate colours. *Pholcus phalangoides* is brown with mottled patterns on the abdomen.
Toxicity. The toxin of the Daddy Long-legs can quickly stun its prey. However, its fangs are so tiny that they cannot bite through the dermal layer of human skin and its minute poison sac holds too little toxin to be of any consequence.
Distribution. Daddy Long-legs are found worldwide and are perhaps the most common of all spiders in Australia. The best known and most common species in the southern half and coastal regions of Australia are those of the genus *Pholcus*.
Habitat. Daddy Long-legs are most frequently seen in or near human habitats.

A female Daddy Long-legs *Pholcus phalangoides*, body length 9 mm.

Their tangled web is an irregular mass of silk, usually hung in a sheltered position such as the corners of ceilings, garages and workshops or behind furniture, shelves and picture-frames.

Prey capture. The web itself is dry and is designed not so much as a snare but as a retreat while the spider awaits prey. The moment an unwary insect ventures within capture range, the spider wraps it in silk and gives a lingering bite until its struggling ceases. It may consume its prey right away or store it for later. I have often seen other species of male spiders (particularly Black House spiders) in their search for females becoming entangled in these webs, and quickly pounced upon and packaged by the deceptively frail-looking Daddy Long-legs.

GUM-FOOTED TANGLE-WEB
Family Theridiidae

RED-BACK COMB-FOOTED	*Latrodectus hasselti* (Thorell 1870)
	Latrodectus = adorned bandit

Description. In Australia the Red-back spider *Lactrodectus hasselti* is now generally recognised as being the same species as New Zealand's Katipo or Night Stinger, and America's Black Widow. This species is the only representative of the genus in Australia. The male Red-back is so tiny (a mere 3 mm long) compared with the large female (14 mm), that he is commonly mistaken for a baby spider when seen about the female's website.

L. hasselti has a satiny,

A female Red-back, *Latrodectus hasselti*.

black or dark brown pea-shaped body, supported on long shiny legs. It has a glossy carapace, and a black abdomen which usually has a broad orange, red or scarlet dorsal stripe along its length (although completely black forms are found). Splotches, spots and dashes occur on other species, but the red stripe of the Red-back is unmistakable. The ventral surface of the female also bears a bright red mark in the shape of an hourglass.

Toxicity. Only the female is dangerous to humans—the male's fangs are too tiny to penetrate human skin. These spiders show little aggression and, if threatened, curl up and fall to the ground. Most Red-back bites occur when the spider is accidentally picked up or trapped against the hand or body when cleaning out rubbish from a workshop or garden. Although no-one in Australia has died from a bite in 40 years (an effective antivenom was developed in 1956), the venom of this species has proved fatal, so the spider must always be treated with caution. Though the female's bite injects only a tiny amount of venom it can cause serious illness, as the poison attacks the nervous system. Medical attention should be sought as soon as possible.

Distribution. The genus *Latrodectus* is found on warm-climate continents. In Australia *L. hasselti* can be found in all regions, including Tasmania and the Simpson Desert.

Habitat. *L. hasselti* prefers dry habitats, ranging from sclerophyll forests to deserts. The greatest number of Red-backs, however, are found among buildings and they have adapted to live in close association with us. Hundreds of people are bitten by these spiders every year in Australia and many of these bites occur in outhouses. Letterboxes and the undersides of seats are also favourite haunts. The Redbacks' gravitation towards urban habitat means that fewer are now encountered in native bushland. After a house has been empty for two years or more, the number of Red-back occupants diminishes. The Katipo of New Zealand is often found inside hollow driftwood, seaweed and debris washed up on beaches.

Prey capture. Our electric lights, shelter and abundance of food scraps attract their prey—moths, flies, beetles, cockroaches and mosquitoes. The gum-footed threads of the tangled web snap back and hold the prey suspended. As it struggles, it soon finds itself stuck fast to adjacent threads. Wandering male Funnel-webs and Trapdoors are frequently ensnared and devoured by Red-backs.

UNREFINED WHEEL-WEB
Family Uloboridae, genus *Uloborus*

The family Uloboridae may represent a link between the Apprentice and Master Weavers. Like the Master Weavers, the Uloborids (Feather-footed spiders) all build wheel-webs with silk, but unlike the Master Weavers they have a calimistrum and a cribellum and the silk they use to build their snares is cribellate. While not attaining the refinements of the Master Weavers' webs, the genus *Uloborus* has nonetheless accomplished the most advanced form of cribellate snare design for the Apprentice Weavers. The web is not a complete wheel-web and usually looks a little clumsy and asymmetrical.

Description. The Uloborids are small to medium-sized, rarely exceeding 12 mm in body length. Most cannot walk on a flat surface but move about on their silken threads very nimbly.

Tent-web, early form of wheel-web, e.g. Araneidae.

A Feather-legged (Uloborid) spider in her wheel-web.

Uloborids are distinguished by their four eyes, divided cribellum, and very long forelegs, whereas spiders of the genus *Miagrammopes* are readily distinguished by their elongated, spindle-shaped abdomens and long, heavily built forelegs. Uloborids have four eyes, set in pairs either side of the small carapace, and a divided cribellum.

Toxicity. Since these spiders do not have poison glands, they are entirely harmless to humans.

Distribution. A typical representative of this family is *Zosis geniculatus* (formerly *Uloborus geniculatus*), a worldwide species that has spread right across the southern portion of Australia and is often found in dry, draughty situations around human habitation. However, most of the species in this family favour sheltered locations in warmer regions and are found in tropical New South Wales and Queensland.

Habitat. Uloborids commonly congregate in large numbers, often in hollow trees, stumps, or shallow sandstone caves, or beneath rock ledges—sometimes under houses and sheds. Their snares may be massed with numerous spiders sharing the tangled silk and with insect prey caught up in the labyrinth of sticky threads.

Prey capture. Spiders of the genus *Miagrammopes* are particularly interesting, as they have abandoned the wheel-web entirely—despite belonging to the Uloboridae family. They have developed a highly specialised method of capturing insect prey with a single thread. One end of this thread is very sticky and held taut by the spider's forelegs; the other end is attached to a nearby branch or leaf. as soon as an insect crawls or flies into the sticky, taut thread, the spider lets go of it. The thread springs back and the slackness of the line quickly entangles the prey. The spider has only to swathe it in silk and feed on it at leisure.

MASTER WEAVERS

In Australia the Master Weavers group consists of 6 families, 36 genera and 340 described species and represents about 17% of Australia's described spiders. The family Araneidae, which includes 90% of this group, has been greatly reshuffled and many species are now described under new names.

Most of us have beheld a dew-covered 'wheel' of silk hanging from the bushes and glistening in the morning sun. These magnificent engineering feats and web designs are snares made by the Master Weavers. They all build wheel-webs and their method of prey capture is far and away the most successful in terms of energy efficiency. Built between the flight paths of insects, these two-dimensional snares, with their symmetrical 'wheel', economise on silk, time and energy. Having eliminated the need to hunt for prey, Master Weavers rely entirely upon silk for every aspect of their lives.

The wheel-web is built with mathematical precision. By comparison with all other snare constructions, it has distinct advantages. It spans generous areas with the minimum of silk; its design allows the spider to move along the geometric pattern of radii while making minimal contact with the sticky spiral. When any portion of the web is touched by prey the vibrations are immediately relayed to the hub, where the spider waits patiently for its food to arrive.

The structure of wheel-webs vary with genera. The wheel shape itself may be complete or incomplete. Some species incorporate extra threads to form a stabilamentum to help strengthen the web. This is particularly necessary for spiders such as the St Andrew's Cross which violently shake the web when threatened, or to tangle insect prey further.

A Master Weaver in her wheel-web.

Golden Orb-weaving spiders build wheel-web snares so strong that small birds can become entangled and held fast. Others incorporate leaves or snail shells to serve as shelter and brood chambers; others modify and reserve a web portion as a disposal area for the dried remains of insects and leaf litter to camouflage themselves at the hub. Most wheel-webs hang vertically, but some are built on an incline or horizontally among shrubs and grasses. All, however, are variations upon a basic design. Silk lines, each attached to a branch or rock, form the main framework. From the hub of the web the spider then trails 'spokes' or radii at regular intervals. Some species spin a set of spokes, others leave a section open to incorporate other structures such as platforms.

The spider then creates a spiral of dry silk scaffolding around the radii from the centre to the outermost peripheral point. Then it retraces its steps and removes the scaffolding by ingestion, replacing each spoke with highly elastic silk coated with sticky glue. This newly laid thread distributes the viscid coating into regularly spaced tiny beads of sticky silk. The spider continues tying new thread in this fashion until it reaches the hub.

The Master Weavers demonstrate some amazing abilities. They have developed an impressive vocabulary of signals, which they transmit along the threads. By plucking, shaking or strumming, they communicate with one another. This is vital to courtship rituals, where males relay their intentions along the lines of the web. They quickly learn to ignore the vibrations of a tuning fork held against the web, and when strong winds threaten to destroy it I have seen *Eriophora* weight the bottom of the framework with stones or wood before severing the web's anchor points, allowing it free movement so as to remain intact. Perhaps the most impressive of all is the fact that when two wheel-weaving spiders were taken on board America's Skylab to see if they could spin their wheel-webs without gravity, these spidernauts managed the feat undaunted.

HORIZONTAL WHEEL-WEB

FOUR-JAWED OR LONG-JAWED

Family Tetragnathidae, genus *Tetragnatha*

All the members of this group are very slender-bodied and long-legged. The palps are also very long and appear leg-like. The males use this feature to advantage during mating.

Description. The spiders of this family are easily distinguished by their extremely long chelicerae which project well forward on the head. Australian Tetragnathidae consist of two genera and 24 described species, most of which are placed in the genus *Tetragnatha*. The female and male *Tetragnatha rubiventris* are similar to one another in size, measuring 12 mm and 10mm long respectively.

Toxicity. Regardless of their huge chelicerae, which are used during mating, the spiders of this family are completely harmless to humans. When disturbed, they either quickly retire to the nearest reed, stem or twig and sit still until danger passes, or drop on their safety-line to the ground and remain motionless.

Distribution. These spiders are usually found in eastern Australia, particularly in coastal regions of New South Wales and Queensland.

Habitat. *Tetragnatha* occur in damp woodlands, open sclerophyll forests and marshy swampland. They normally suspend their

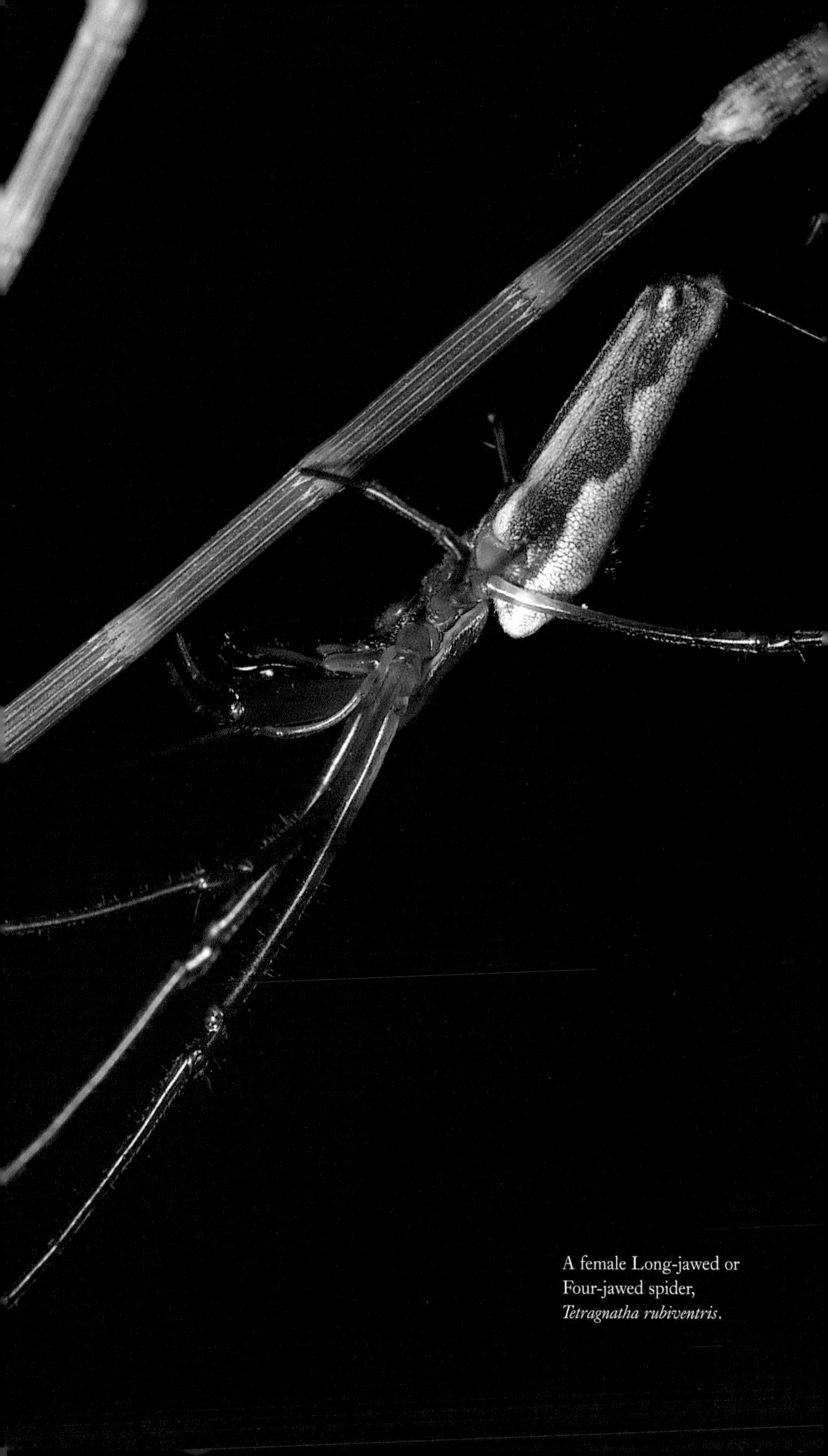

A female Long-jawed or Four-jawed spider, *Tetragnatha rubiventris*.

horizontal wheel-webs between reeds and waterlilies, overhanging the water surface by a few centimetres. When water is scarce, their wheel-webs can also be found in long grass.

Prey capture. Their food is chiefly light-bodied, gnat-like insects that abound near water and fly during the evening. As the flying insects alight on water iris or lilypads to drink or perform mating rituals, they fly straight up into the sticky spiral snare and the spider's gaping jaws.

INCLINED WHEEL-WEB
Family Araneidae

GOLDEN ORB-WEAVING

Subfamily Nephilinae: *Nephila edulis, Nephila maculata* and *Nephila ornata*

The Golden orb-weaving spiders have acquired their popular name because of their golden wheel-web snares, which are sometimes found strung in backyard gardens, in fruit trees, and across pathways and driveways above car height.

Only females build these snares—the males spend the greater portion of their lives on the outskirts of the webs. These spiders do not tear their webs down, but continually repair them and renew them only when absolutely necessary. When threatened, these spiders vigorously shake the entire web, transforming it into a shimmering golden blur, the spider seemingly disappearing within the vibrating threads.

Small birds such as finches and wrens are

The huge female (45 mm) and the tiny male (6 mm) Golden Orb-weaving spiders, *Nephila maculata*. Photo: Joseph Shemesh.

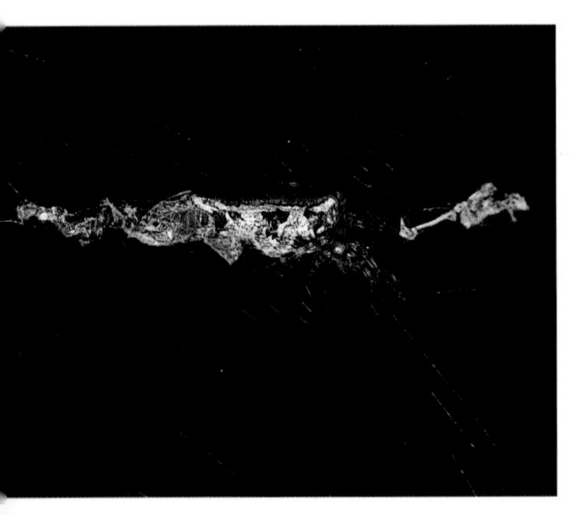

The female *Cyclosa insulana* camouflages her snare with a horizontal centre band of debris.

A juvenile Golden Orb-weaving spider, *Nephila ornata*, with prey. Photo: Eugene Hodgens.

sometimes ensnared to become a meal of the huge *N. maculata*.

Unlike most Master Weavers, the Golden Orb-weaving webs are homesites 24 hours a day. They are also used for mating and waste disposal sites, and homes for the tiny Quicksilver spiders of the genus *Argyodes* (family Theridiidae). These Quicksilver spiders have abandoned snare-making and cohabit with many species of Master Weavers. This relationship serves both parties extremely well: the *Nephila* supplies the Quicksilver spiders with an abundance of tiny insect prey, too small for itself, while the Quicksilver spiders keep their host's web clean of clutter and disease. The Tailed spider, *Arachnura higginsi,* also has a symbiotic relationship with the Quicksilver, and so do several other species of Apprentice and Master Weavers.

Description. The females of *Nephila edulis* and *Nephila ornata* measure 24 mm long, while the males measure a mere 6 mm long, and are brown with large palps. The huge female of *Nephila maculata* can measure up to 45 mm long, has a carapace covered in golden hairs and an abdomen covered in silver-grey hairs. The legs may be banded in yellow-orange and black. The male *N. maculata* is only 6 mm long and so small that it is commonly mistaken for a baby spider. It is usually red-brown to dark-brown.

The giant *N. maculata* females are the largest known spiders to construct geometrical snares, and small birds sometimes become entangled in them. The species also has the widest distribution range of the *Nephila* genus and is found in northern Queensland, Papua New Guinea, Polynesia, Malaysia, Bali and India. Certain Pacific Island and Papua New Guinea people use the strong snares to make fishing scoops.

Toxicity. Despite the size and appearance of the females, they are all completely harmless to humans. *Nephila* are normally preoccupied with their own affairs and would have to be roughly handled before biting in self-defence. Their fangs are not designed to bite large vertebrates but are a real asset when manipulating prey in the web.

Distribution. The distribution range of these handsome spiders is eastern Australia, mainly along the coast, from Victoria to Cape York in far north Queensland, but they are also found in many inland areas. *Nephila edulis* is found in temperate and tropical regions; *N. maculata* has a tropical distribution only; and *N. ornata* is both a temperate and tropical spider. *N. maculata* has the distinction of having been given 14 different names by different authors, due to the species' wide distribution range.

Habitat. The wheel-web snares of the Golden Orb-weaving spiders glisten unmistakably in the sunlight. The almost vertical wheel-web can measure more than 1 metre across and is frequently strung high above the ground, in the understorey of sclerophylous forests and woodlands. However, it is more commonly strung between small trees a couple of metres off the ground. It is sometimes found in backyard gardens, in fruit trees or strung across a driveway, above car height.

Prey capture. Unlike the garden spiders of the genus *Eriophora*, the Golden Orb-weaving spiders leave intact their scaffolding of dry spiral threads, to help strengthen the snare against the violent struggles of huge wood moths, cicadas, large beetles, locusts and even tiny birds and bats.

VERTICAL WHEEL-WEB
Families Araneidae and Argiopidae

ST ANDREW'S CROSS	*Argiope keyserlingi* (Karsch 1878)
	Family Argiopidae

Of Australia's 25 described species of *Argiope*, the St Andrew's Cross Spider, *A. keyserlingi*, is the best known and most strikingly coloured.

Description. This species is well known partly because of its zig-zag ribbons of silk, which fill four sections of the web between opposite radii, and partly because of its striking appearance. The female is 12-15 mm long; the tiny male is 5 mm, and red-brown. The abdomen of the female is striped with yellow, red, white and black hairs and the carapace is covered with a close pile of silver-grey hair. These bands of colour can be made dull or vibrant by the spider either expanding or retracting its abdomen, thereby altering the refraction of light striking on the pile. When the spider is startled or threatened, raised hairs increase the colour vibrancy. When the spider is resting in her snare, she appears to have

A female Saint Andrew's Cross, *Argiope keyerslingi*, with bundled prey.

A female Saint Andrew's Cross, *Argiope keyserlingi*, admired for the beautiful design of her wheel-web.

four legs. In fact, she is holding her eight legs in four pairs, each pair lying along an arm of the distinctive cross.

Toxicity. These spiders are completely harmless to humans, as are most—if not all—spiders that live in the open.

Distribution. *Argiope keyserlingi* is found in warm regions, particularly tropical coastal areas of Australia. *Argiope aemula, A. picta* and *A. trifasciata* are closely related species and sometimes confused with the St Andrew's Cross spider; however, none of these build the distinctive cross. *A. aemula* is found from New South Wales to Cape York in Queensland, *A. picta* is found from Victoria to north Queensland, and *A. trifasciata* occurs throughout Australia, including Tasmania.

Habitat. *A. keyserlingi* normally constructs its wheel-web a couple of metres off the ground, amongst shrubs and tall grasses growing along waterways, where insect prey is plentiful. Another of their bush habitats is in the cutaways created by water courses on hills and slopes.

Prey capture. Butterflies, damselflies, flies, bees, day-flying moths, grasshoppers and beetles are frequently caught in the sticky web. The spider has been observed to grasp her snare at the hub and shake it so vigoroursly that she becomes a blur. This dramatic movement certainly helps to further entangle large insect prey, and probably also distracts would-be predators.

SPINY	Family Araneidae, genus *Gasteracantha*
	minax = threatening, projecting

These colourful and bizarrely-shaped spiders occur in tropical and sub-tropical regions and Australia has several species. Their body shape and colours are extraordinary.

Description. The abdomen is always very broad (usually far broader than long) and shielded with a very hard cuticle, like that of an insect. Six stout spines, usually long and sharp, project from the border of the abdomen. All *Gasteracantha* species are short-legged. The female is 6 mm long, the male 4 mm.

Toxicity. All species of Spiny Wheel-web Weaving spiders are entirely harmless to humans and usually try to move out of harm's way.

Distribution. The species *G. minax* is found in all states of Australia including Tasmania and on numerous islands off the coast. I have seen them in their thousands in southern areas of New South Wales during the summer months of January and February.

Habitat. Large colonies of these spiders often overlap one another among shrubbery in the bushland. I normally find them most prevalent in shrubby woodlands, especially near swamps and creeks. Their wheel-webs overlap and are normally built a metre or two from the ground.

Prey capture. These spiders prey on an enormous population of flying insects, particularly flies, during the summer. Although spiders do not seem to have any of the social organisation so typical of ants, bees, wasps and termites, there are communities of spiders that benefit all participants—prey is shared regardless of whose web it landed in.

A female Two-spined *Poecilopachus australiae*, one of the few spiders that can change the colouring of its abdomen very quickly.

A tropical female Spiny, *Gasteracantha fornicata*. Australia's first documented spider was a Spiny collected from Cooktown, Nth Queensland, by Joseph Banks.

A colony of Spiny wheel-weavers (*Gasteracantha*) in open woodland. Photo: Christine Urquhart.

VERTICALLY REFINED WHEEL-WEB
Family Araneidae

WHEEL-WEAVING GARDEN	*Eriophora transmarina* (Keyserling 1865)
	transmarina = over water or seas

All members of the genus *Eriophora* are known as Wheel-weaving Garden spiders and make the 'typical' and 'perfect' wheel-web. They are common in parks, home gardens and bushland throughout Australia and include some of the best-known wheel-web weavers. Australia has well over 100 species, of which the most commonly known is the large *Eriophora transmarina*, coloured in subtle hues to match its surroundings.

Description. This species is heavily built and hairy. A variety of colours and patterns is characteristic of the species—apparently according to its surroundings. Many individuals have a foliate pattern outlined in a dark colour around the margin of the abdomen. Some have a median white stripe or arrow-head design or dark brown stripe running dorsally along the abdomen. Colouring varies from grey-brown, rusty-red, brick-red, yellow-ochre, olive green, or beige, uniform or mottled.

E. transmarina has two distinct humps on the outer margins of its abdomen and two smaller ones below these at the rear. A gravid female can measure over 30 mm long, and its bulky abdomen alone can measure 20 mm long (and almost as broad), dwarfing its carapace and limbs. The male measures 15 to 20 mm long.

Toxicity. The Wheel-weaving Garden spider is completely non-poisonous to humans. When startled or disturbed it does its best to leave the scene without fuss as quickly as possible. Usually it quickly ascends its web to huddle among leaves,

A rarely seen wheel-weaving *Eriophora* species.

A fine example of the Wheel-weaving Garden spider's web. It consists of over 20 m of silk, 0.005 mm in diameter, which can support 4,000 times its own weight.
Photo: Anthony Saunders.

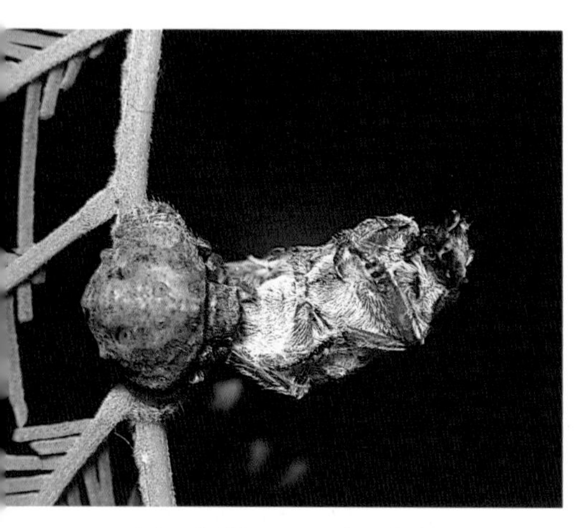

A female Wrap-around, *Dolophones maximus* (8 mm). This uncommonly seen wheel-weaver camouflages herself during the day by wrapping her concave abdomen around a twig or branch. Here she eats a cockchafer snared during the night.

E. transmarina sometimes has a white dorsal stripe along the abdomen.

Eriophora heroine (16 mm), a Wheel-weaver common in gardens and bushland throughout Qld, NSW, Vic. and Tas.

branches or whatever shelter is available. Sometimes it simply drops to the ground on its safety-line, remains motionless until danger has passed, then ascends to the hub again; if the web is badly torn, it retires for the night.

Distribution. The species is found in every state of Australia and the Northern Territory, and in a wide range of habitats. Representatives of the genus are found worldwide.

Habitat. In their natural bush habitat their wheel-webs are often strung well above the ground between trees across forest trails, creeks or streams. Such strategically placed snares provide abundant opportunities to catch a wide range of night-flying insects. Although cryptically coloured, most of these spiders huddle beneath leaves or bark during their daylight repose. When those adorned with white leave their snares, they are in constant danger of being discovered and eaten. These unusual white individuals cannot change colouring as the brown and grey forms can—a very strange inheritance, considering the protection of leaf-like patterns which their brothers and sisters enjoy.

Prey capture. The Garden spider is sensitive to the slightest vibration of its snare. Immediately an insect hits the snare, it dashes out to claim its prize. Once the insect is securely bundled, the spider drags it into the hub and either consumes it or hangs it nearby for a later supper. When prey is plentiful the spider may release a large insect by severing threads rather than have its web destroyed. During leaner times, however, the spider makes every effort to capture even dangerously large prey such as bush crickets and longicorn beetles. On such an event the spider approaches the prey with caution, as the sticky spiral doesn't hold powerful mandibles closed for long. Combing out copious swathes of silk and enveloping its catch, the artful spider rotates the prey between its shorter third pairs of legs until it has wrapped it up to look like a miniature Egyptian mummy.

LEAF-CURLING
Family Araneidae

INCOMPLETE WHEEL-WEB WEAVERS WITH RETREAT INCORPORATED

Phonognatha graeffei (Rainbow 1896)

The wheel-webs of these weavers are often seen in our gardens, especially during late summer and autumn. They are well known because they use curled leaf retreats within their snares—the only spiders to consistently do so.

Unlike the Golden Orb-weaving spiders, these weavers often replace their wheel-webs, but like them, they construct snares with an untidy tangle of threads forming a platform either side of the central radii. With the greater portion of the snare hanging beneath the hub, the wheel-web of the Leaf-curling spider is not complete or symmetrical. The main frame is set between bushes and up to 60 or more radial threads are erected. The upper portion, well above the curled leaf, is criss-crossed by numerous random threads that support the main frame.

Description. The two most commonly found species in eastern Australia are *Phonognatha graeffei* and *Phonognatha sylvicola*. The *P. graeffei* is an attractively coloured spider: its abdomen is decorated in a marbled pattern of white dots, and it has green and yellow patches on its dorsal surface. The cephalothorax, carapace and limbs are

The Leaf-curling spider *Phonognatha graeffei* (body length 8-10 mm) cleverly disguises its retreat.

A female *Phonognatha graeffei* with prey.

orange-brown. The female is 14 mm long, the male is 10 mm.

Toxicity. This spider is completely harmless to humans. It may nip a finger in self-defence if you inadvertently handle it without garden gloves. It is more than happy to remain inside its curled leaf retreat until it has the good fortune to ensnare a lively insect that has just hit the net.

Distribution. *P. sylvicola* and *P. graeffei* are found in south-eastern Australia, particularly New South Wales, although they also occur in Victoria and Tasmania. *P. melania* is found in the south-western forests of Western Australia. The form of *P. melania* looks remarkably similar to that of *P. graeffei* and may be the same species. They have become isolated from one another by the drying of the continent and the consequent paucity of forest between the states.

Habitat. These spiders particularly like to suspend their snares along paths and insect trails in woodlands and open forests, usually on shrubs within 2 metres of the ground. Suburban gardens are also favoured, particularly near tall paling fences. Walkways in parks and gardens, especially where undisturbed shrubbery is thriving, continually yield a generous bounty of flying insects for these little Master Weavers, who are prepared for such activity day or night.

P. graeffei have perhaps evolved their webs one step further than the other wheel-web spiders, even though they are incomplete. They have adopted the clever tactic of converting their snare to a well-disguised retreat by using a curled leaf—sometimes a scrap of paper, piece of bark or even an empty snail shell. The leaf retreat is held firmly in place with numerous strands of silk.

Prey capture. The Leaf-curling spider, a courageous little creature, readily confronts large insects ensnared in its wheel-web. It rushes out from its leaf shelter immediately an insect hits the net. I have often witnessed these spiders assessing their catch before handling it—moving carefully around a bee, for example, to avoid its sting. Having assessed it, the spider proceeds, with great agility, to swathe its prey in ribbon silk produced from the aciniform glands. Using its shorter third pair of legs, the spider revolves its prey around and around until all flailing limbs are immobilised by the silk binding. At this stage, the spider bites the insect until all struggling ceases. If the insect proves too large or dangerous to handle, the spider severs the threads holding it and lets it drop to the ground, rather than have the snare torn apart.

GLOSSARY

Abdomen: Also called the **opisthosoma**. The rear segment of a spider's body which carries the reproductive organs, respiratory equipment, digestive and excretive system, silk glands and **spinnerets**.

Aciniform glands: Produce ribbon silk for swathing prey, and decorative silk bands for snares and egg sacs. Also used for the **stabilamentum**.

Aggregrate glands: Produce viscid (adhesive) thread for ensnaring prey, e.g. in spiral snares.

Ampullate glands: Produce dry silk for drag-lines, bridge-lines, the radii of wheel-web snares, and balloons.

Anal tubercle: A small rounded projection bearing the anal orifice at the rear of the abdomen.

Antivenom: A specific combination of proteins which make the blood system react by producing antibodies to combat a specific toxin.

Anterior spinnerets: Those that appear nearest the cephalothorax when the abdomen is viewed ventrally (from beneath).

Antivenene: Former term for antivenom.

Apophysis: A protrusion larger than a spine, situated on male spiders' palps and legs—for example, the spur-like protrusions on the tibia of the second pair of legs of the male Funnel-web (*Atrax robustus*).

Arachnology: The study of animals of the phylum Arthropoda, class Arachnida.

Araneology: The study of spiders; creatures that make up the order Araneae, distinguished from all other creatures by abdominal spinnerets.

Araneomorphae: This suborder encompasses modern or 'true' spiders.

Attachment disc: The point where silken thread is attached to sand, clay, leaf bark or rock.

Book-lungs: Respiration organs, situated on the ventral surface of the abdomen. Primitive spiders have two sets, Modern spiders have one.

Bowl web: A lattice-sheet web of dry silk formed by the family Linyphiidae.

Calimistrum: The one or two rows of curved, toothed bristles on the fourth metatarsus, used for combing out silk from the **cribellum**.

Caput: The portion of **cephalothorax** (or **prosoma**) that refers to the head section. This division is not clear cut as it is with insects.

Carapace: The **chitinous** dorsal plate of the **cephalothorax**, bearing the eyes and head and extending back to where it meets the abdomen.

Cephalothorax: The portion that unites the head and **thorax**, covered by the carapace. Sometimes referred to as a **prosoma**.

Chelicerae: Often referred to as the jaws; consists of two segments—a fang and a fang base.

Chitinous: The strong, flexible, fibrous material (like cellulose) that forms the exoskeleton of spiders and insects.

Colulus: A conical bump—the remnant of the **cribellum**.

Comb: A group of stiff spines or **setae**.

Coxa: The basal segment of **palps** and legs, situated close to the **labium** and **sternum** on the ventral surface. The first **palp** joints form a pair of plates used for crushing prey.

Cribellate glands: Produce the highly elastic, **hackled**, woolly silk used by cribellate spiders, e.g. Black House spiders.

Cribellum: The organ that makes hackled snares; it serves as a sieve for the raw silk that is combed out into woolly bands.

Cuspules: Tooth-like serrations on a spider's mouthparts.

Cuticle: See **sclerotin**.

Diaxial: Refers to the chelicerae; it means that fangs are placed opposing each other, as they are in Modern spiders.

Dimorphism: Occurs when the male and female of a single species each takes a distinct form.

Dome-web: Dome-shaped, dry silk sheet web.

Dorsal: Upper, as in upper surface.

Drag-line: The silk trailing from a spider's posterior. Often called a **safety-line**, as it can save the spider from falling.

Embolus: The male spider's spiny tube through which sperm passes from the **palpal** bulb.

Endite: See **Maxilla**.

Entelegyne: The female's vulva. It has separate openings for the insemination of the **epigynum**, and fertilisation ducts from her **spermathecae**.

Epigynum: The female's reproductive organs—a complex, chitinous structure. A single opening connects the ovaries and a pair of openings form the **spermathecae** pockets into which the male spider discharges his sperm-filled palps. The epigynum is not externally visible in Primitive spiders.

Epistome: Upper lip bordering the spider's mouth. Also called the **rostrum**.

Exoskeleton: The horny outer covering of a spider or insect body.

Fang groove: Where the fangs fold away when not in use. In some families the borders of this groove have teeth arrangements; in others they are smooth.

Femur: The third segment of the limbs, as numbered from the **ventral** base of the body.

Flagelliform glands: Produce silk for making the gluey globules that weight the threads of Bolas spiders.

Fovea: A small pit in the carapace for the muscle attachment of the sucking stomach.

Gonophore: The entrance to the insemination duct of the female's epigynum.

Hackled: Refers to the woolliness of cribellate spider's silk.

Haplogyne: Describes the vulva that has a single duct for insemination and fertilisation.

Hypochilomorphae: The suborder often referred to as the living link between Mygalomorphae and Araneomorphae.

Instar: A stage of spider or insect development between two moults.

Labium: Plate structure on the **ventral** surface of the cephalothorax. It forms the floor of the mouth and is fixed to the sternum by its posterior edge.

Labrum: The upper lip, on the anterior **ventral** part of the cephalothorax.

Lace-webs: Cribellate silken snares, embroidered with lacy patterns: used by the family Desidae (Black House spiders).

Laterigrade: Legs pointing sideways rather than to the front or rear, as on Huntsman and Crab spiders. Such spiders move sideways and can easily creep into narrow cracks.

Maxilla: Sometimes called the **endite**; it forms the first segment of the coxa of the **palp**.

Median eyes: The eyes between each row.

Median spinnerets: The small central pair of **spinnerets** often obscured by the larger spinnerets.

Metatarsus: The sixth segment of limbs, as numbered from the base of the body.

Moult: The process of shedding exoskeletons between instars.

Mygalomorphae: The suborder of Primitive or straight-jawed spiders; includes Trapdoor, Funnel-web and Brushfooted Trapdoor spiders.

Necrosis: Death of tissue. ('Necrotic' means 'tissue-dissolving').

Nursery web: The nest or nursery site of the *Dolomedes* spider.

Ocellus (pl. **ocelli**): A simple eye, as opposed to the compound eye of most insects. Insects often have three ocelli in addition to their compound eyes; spiders normally have six to eight ocelli.

Opisthosoma: The posterior division of a spider's body, usually called the abdomen.

Orb web: Wheel web, as constructed by Master Weavers.

Palps: The second pair of appendages that occur after the chelicerae, either side of the mouth.

Paraxial: Describes fangs when they lie parallel to one another and project horizontally, as on Funnel-webs.

Patella: The fourth segment of limbs, as numbered from the base of the body.

Pedicel: The flexible waist or tub joining the two major segments of a spider's body; the much reduced first segment of the abdomen.

Pedipalp: See **palp**.

Peg-teeth: Teeth set in the sockets of the chelicerae.

Pheromone: A chemical substance produced by female spiders; emitted as a subtle vapour, often to attract males during the breeding season.

Phylum: All animals belong to one of about 30 large groups, each of which is called a phylum.

Platform web: A fine, latticed sheet web of dry silk shaped like a hammock.

Prograde: Describes an arrangement of leg pairs: pairs one and two point forward and pairs three and four point backward, so that the spider moves forward.

Prolateral: The surface nearest the inner side of the spider's anterior end.

Prosoma: See **cephalothorax**.

Pyriform glands: Produce a liquid silk used for attaching a disc to a surface, and for radii and web framework.

Raptorial: Strong spiny forelimbs used for grasping and crushing prey, e.g. as found with praying mantids.

Rastellum: A series of short teeth or spines along the basal joint of the chelicerae, used for digging burrows; common on Trapdoors.

Retrolateral: The outer surface nearest the spider's posterior.

Rostrum: See **epistome**.

Safety-line: See **drag-line**.

Sclerotin: The cuticle or hard outer skeleton of an insect or spider.

Scopula: A band of close hairs forming a brush.

Scutum: The sclerotised plate on the abdomen of certain spiders, e.g. Spiny spiders.

Serrula: A row of tiny saw-like teeth on the front outside edge of the first segment of the palp of most spiders; used for chewing and cutting.

Seta: A slender hair or a bristle structure on body or limb.

Sheet web: A closely matted, curved or flat web made of dry silk, with a retreat tube or funnel in one corner.

Spermathecae: The female spider's pair of pockets for collecting sperm from the male. The pocket are connected to the ovaries by an opening.

Spine: A cuticle structure stouter than a bristle.

Spinnerets: The silk-producing organs or spinning tubes, ventrally placed on the abdomen. Ancient spiders had eight of these, but existing forms (depending on the species) now have only six, four or a single pair.

Spiracles: The tracheal openings on the ventral surface of the abdomen.

Sprung web: Tangle web that snaps on contact with prey; e.g. the Red-back's web.

Stabilamentum: A band of dense silk laid across or around a wheel-web, apparently to stabilise it.

Sternum: The ventral plate of the cephalothorax, scalloped to accommodate the coxae of limbs. The coxae and labium surround this plate.

Substrate: Any surface underneath the subject.

Tangle web: Scattered, criss-crossed threads supporting a framework, as seen in the webs of Daddy long-legs and Red-backs.

Tarsus: The outer segment of the leg or palp; the fifth segment of limbs, as numbered from the body.

Thorax: The part of the body to which the limbs are attached.

Toxicology: The scientific study of poisons, their effects, antidotes and detection.

Toxin: The component of venom that makes a spider's bite inflict ill effects.

Trap-lines: See **sprung web**.

Trichobothria: The sensory hairs set into sockets on the limbs of certain spiders (e.g. Black House spiders) for quickly locating entangled prey.

Trip-lines: Haphazard radial threads that relay prey movement to the burrow or retreat.

Tubercles: Low, rounded projections or nodules on which the eyes of certain spiders are set to improve vision scope.

Venom: Fluid produced by the venom glands, containing an assortment of chemicals—some help to break down (predigest) the tissues of prey into an emulsified state. Toxin is only a minor component of venom.

Ventral: Undeside or lower; usually refers to surface.

FURTHER READING

Brunet, B. 1983, *One Step Closer, Please*, View Productions, Sydney.

Brunet, B. 1987, 'Feasting at the Manna Gum', *Circ. Ent. Section*, Royal Zool. Soc. NSW, No. 55, pp. 44-5.

Brunet, B. 1994, *The Silken Web, A Natural History of Australian Spiders*, Reed Books, Sydney.

Clyne, D. 1969, *A Guide to Australian Spiders*, Nelson, Melbourne.

Clyne, D. 1979, *The Garden Jungle*, Collins, Sydney.

Davies, V.T. 1986, *Australian Spiders: Araneae, Collection, Preservation and Identification*, Queensland Museum.

Forster, R.R. and Forster, L.M. 1973, *New Zealand Spiders, An Introduction*, Collins, Auckland.

Gray, M.R. 1986, 'A Systematic Study of the Funnel-web Spiders (Mygalomorphae: Hexathelidae: Atracinae)', PhD Thesis, Macquarie University, Sydney.

Gray, M.R. 1988, 'Distribution of the Funnel-web Spiders', *Toxic Plants and Animals: a guide for Australia*, Queensland Museum, Brisbane, pp. 312-20.

Kaston, B.J. 1966, 'Evolution of the web', *Nat. Hist.*, vol. 75, pp. 26-33.

Main, B.Y. 1976, *Spiders*, Austn Naturalists Library, Collins, Sydney.

Main, B.Y. 1985, 'Arachnida: Mygalomorphae', in Walton, D.W. (ed.), *Zoological Catalogue of Australia*, No. 3, pp. 1-48, Australian Government Printing Service, Canberra.

Mascord, R. 1989, *Australian Spiders in Colour*, Reed Books, Sydney.

McKeown, K.C. 1963, *Australian Spiders*, Angus & Robertson, Sydney.

Raven, R.J. 1985, 'The spider infraorder Mygalomorphae (Araneae): cladistics and systematics', *Bull. Am. Mus. Nat. Hist.*, 182, 1-180.

Robinson, M.H. and Robinson, B. 1975, 'Evolution beyond the orb web of the araneid spider *Pasilobus* species, its structure, operation and construction', *Zool. J. Linn. Soc.*, Vol. 5, pp. 301-313.

Sutherland, S.K. 1989, *Venomous Creatures of Australia*, Oxford University Press, Melbourne.

INDEX

ABBREVIATIONS

Primitive Spiders (P)
Ambushers & Anglers (A/A)
Master Weavers (M/W)
Open Range Hunters (O/R)
Apprentice Weavers (A/W)

NOTES